THE NEW CATHEDRAL BASIC READERS

CURRICULUM FOUNDATION SERIES

MORE FRIENDS OLD AND NEW

CATHEDRAL EDITION

The Right Reverend
Monsignor John B. McDowell

Helen M. Robinson, Marion Monroe, A. Sterl Artley

Linguistic Advisor: W. Cabell Greet

Illustrators: Jack White, Bob Childress, Bob Korta, Richard E. Loehle, Rod Ruth

Scott, Foresman and Company
Chicago Atlanta Dallas Palo Alto Fair Lawn, N.J.

Stories

Neighborhood Friends

 Earlier editions of the Second Grade Readers of the Cathedral Basic Reading Program were published by Scott, Foresman and Company in 1923, 1931, 1942, 1947, and 1954.

With Ecclesiastical Approval. Pittsburgh, June 25, 1964.

Animal Friends

Storybook Friends

NEIGHBORHOOD FRIENDS

The New Boy

Mark Winters rolled his bike to the front of the house where his family now lived. Tramp, his dog, watched him.

"Now you stay home, Tramp," Mark said. "You can't go to school with me."

Tramp watched Mark get on his bike.

"I have a new bike, new clothes, a new school, and a new neighborhood," thought Mark. "But no new friends."

As soon as Mark turned onto First Street, Tramp hurried after him.

"Tramp!" Mark cried. "Go home." But Tramp went on running behind the bike.

Mark turned around and began to shout at Tramp again. Suddenly the front wheel of his bike started sliding on some ice, and then both Mark and his bike fell into some dark water that was on the ice.

Mark sat up and looked at Tramp.

"Now see what you've done!" he cried. "Why didn't you stay home as I said?"

Tramp put her tail under her back legs and looked at Mark with big, sad eyes.

"You silly dog," Mark said. "**Now** you're sorry! A lot of good that does!"

Mark picked up his muddy things and got on his bike. "Come on," he called to Tramp. "I've got to go home."

At the house Mark tried both doors, but no one was there. He took Tramp to the back yard and tied the dog to the clothesline. Then he got on his muddy bike and hurried to school.

At school Mark found the right room and walked in. Sister Mary Jean looked at his muddy, wet clothes and cried, "Dear me! Who are you? And what have you done to yourself?"

"I'm Mark Winters. I'm new in this town," Mark said. "While I was on my way to school, my bike began sliding on some ice. I fell into some water."

"You should go home and get out of those muddy clothes," said Sister.

"I did go home," Mark answered. "But I couldn't get in. My mother and father will be away until three o'clock."

Sister looked sadly at Mark. "What are we to do?" she said. "You must get out of those wet, muddy clothes."

"Mark is about as big as I am," Tim Good cried. "He can wear some of my clothes. I live nearby. We'll go home now. It won't take us long."

Tim took Mark to his house, where Mark got some clean clothes.

When the boys got back to school, the children were having reading. Mark sat down and took out his reading book. It was all wet and muddy.

Mark looked at his wet, muddy book. All the children looked, too. Mark's ears started turning red.

Suddenly Sister Mary Jean smiled. David was going over to where Mark sat.

"Here, Mark," David said. "Use my book. I'll sit with Carlos and read from his book with him."

Later a bell rang, and the children with lunches left for the lunchroom. Those who were going home waited for the next bell to ring. Everyone but Mark had a coat on. He had no lunch. He had no money to buy one. He just sat.

Sister said, "Mark, where is your lunch? Didn't you bring one?"

Mark took out his wet, muddy lunch. "This **was** my lunch!" he said sadly.

Katy put her hand up. "Sister," she said. "I'll take Mark home with me. My mother always has enough for one more."

Sister smiled at Katy.

All day long the boys and girls took turns helping Mark whenever he needed it. Then after school they went with Mark and got their bikes. They stopped at Tim's house and waited while Mark got the clothes that had been drying for him. Then Mark and his new friends went riding off to his house.

Mrs. Winters opened the front door when she saw Mark coming.

"Did you have a good day?" she began. Then her eyes got bigger and bigger.

"Mark!" she cried. "Those aren't your clothes. And what in the world happened to your new bike?"

"When I left this morning, I was sad," said Mark. "I had new things but no new friends. Then something happened." And he told about Tramp and how he got all wet and muddy when he fell on the ice.

"It **was** a good day," Mark smiled. "My things don't look new any more. But just look at all my new friends!"

Tommy's Valentines

Ellen Winters was in the family room, getting ready for Valentine's Day. Her little brother was watching.

"Pretty," said Tommy. "I want."

Ellen laughed. "You'll get one on Saint Valentine's Day," she said.

Suddenly the doorbell rang. Ellen hurried to the living room and opened the door. She saw Mrs. Small, a neighbor.

"Come in," Ellen said.

"I've been busy making valentines to send to my sister Jill's children," said Mrs. Small. "I have more than enough, and I thought that you would like some of them."

"How nice," Ellen said. "Thank you, Mrs. Small."

"Here," the woman said. "Take one and eat it. You too, Tommy."

Ellen smiled as she ate the valentine, but Tommy made a funny face.

"Eat valentines?" he asked.

"Oh, Tommy," Ellen said. "There is more than one kind of valentine in the world. Those that Mrs. Small makes are put in an oven and baked."

Tommy put out his hand and took one of the valentines. He looked at it. He smelled it. Then he ate a little.

"Oh, cookie!" he cried. "More, more!"

"Not now," said Mrs. Winters, as she came into the room. "You have enough. We'll keep the others until your brothers come home." She took the cookies and put them on top of the TV. Then she sat down to visit with her neighbor.

"More, more!" cried Tommy.

"No," said his mother. "You ate one. Now go and play."

Tommy's face was very sad, but he left the living room. Ellen sat down to listen to her mother talk with Mrs. Small. After a while, she decided to go back and work on her valentines.

When Ellen went through the door to the family room, she opened her eyes in surprise.

"Mother, come quick!" she called. "Something has happened to all of my valentines. I had cut out lots of them, but I can see only one here now."

Mrs. Winters called back to Ellen. "Maybe Tommy is playing with them in the kitchen," she cried. "Go and see."

Suddenly Ellen called again. "Come quick! Come to the kitchen."

"Look!" Ellen cried, as everyone came running through the kitchen doorway.

"Oh, Tommy!" Mrs. Winters said. "What were you trying to do? You should never open the oven. You may get burned!"

Tommy had a big smile on his face. "Cookies!" he said. "Cookies!"

Ellen laughed, "I told Tommy that Mrs. Small had baked her valentines in the oven. He must have decided that you can really turn paper valentines into cookies if you bake them in that way!"

Play Ball!

"Oh, Pete," called Tim, as he saw his friend about a block away. "Come and play ball. We need another player."

"I don't want to," said Pete, as he came running up. "I really don't."

"We need you!" Tim cried. "Katy Burns told the boys on Green Street that we played better baseball than they did. Now we've got to show them."

"I'm no good," said Pete, turning his face to one side. "You don't want me."

"Come on," Tim said. "We won't have enough players if you don't."

Just then Mark came hurrying up. "I found Carlos," he said. "He's going to get Joseph. David is coming, too. He's bringing Bill Stone. Katy Burns will catch. With you two, we have enough."

"No, we don't," said Tim.

Mark said the names over to himself. Then he laughed. "I left out the best player of all! My brother Jerry!"

"Jerry?" asked Pete. "Do I know him?"

"You will if you come and play ball," Mark answered. "To me, he's the best baseball player in the world."

"I think my mother needs help," said Pete. "I'd better go home and see."

"We'll go and ask her if you can play," said Tim. "This is a big game!"

Pete looked to one side as he walked along. "I can't play baseball," he thought sadly. "I hope Mother needs help."

Pete's mother was in her garden.

"Mrs. Small," Tim cried. "We need Pete for a baseball game in our block. We're playing the boys from Green Street. Pete said he was sure you needed him for work. If you'll let him play, I'll help too when we're through with the game."

"There's nothing for Pete now," Mrs. Small decided. "I hope you have fun."

The boys ran to a lot next to Mr. Hill's house. The game was about to start.

"Jerry, this is Pete," Tim puffed.

"Hello," Jerry said. "We're up to bat first. When Green Street comes up to bat, you go out to right field."

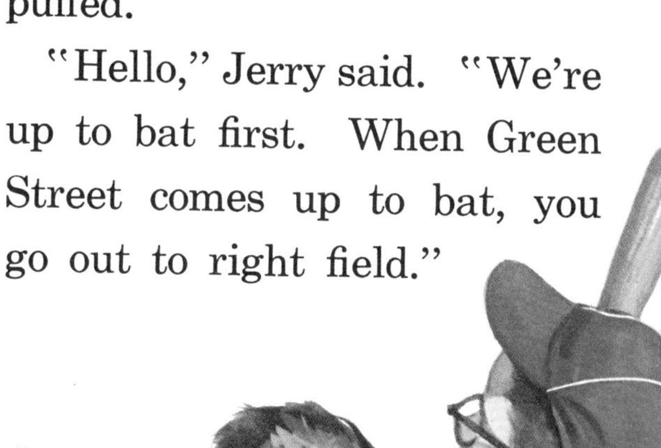

At first, Pete thought only of how he would keep his friends from playing good ball. But as time went by, he found that his side was doing very well. As the end of the playing time came near, the game was six to five. Then the Green Street boys lined up for their last turn at bat.

"I hope they don't get a run," thought Pete. "If not, the game will be ours."

The first two batters couldn't hit Jerry's ball at all. Then each of the next two players made a hit. That put Green Street boys on both first and second.

Another boy from Green Street took his place, ready to bat.

"Come on, Jerry!" Katy Burns cried. "Don't let him hit that ball!"

Jerry smiled. Quick as a flash, the ball left his hand. Bang! The batter hit, and the ball went flying out to right field.

"Get it!" Mark cried from his place at second. "Get that fly!"

Pete raced after the flying ball. Just as he got it, he tripped and fell to the ground. The ball rolled from his hands, and the Green Street boys on first and second began to run for home. Both runs came in before Pete could get the ball back to Jerry.

"The game is ours!" shouted the Green Street boys as they raced down the block.

"We lost," said Katy sadly. She picked up her bat and started with the rest of the players for home.

Soon all had gone but Mark, Pete, and Jerry. The two brothers came to Pete.

"It was a good game," Mark said.

Pete just looked at the ground.

"You didn't mean to trip," Jerry said.

"I just can't play ball!" Pete cried.

"Don't say **can't**!" Mark said. "You can if you try. It was only last year that Jerry began to play baseball. Before that he could do nothing more than watch."

"That's right," said Jerry. "Every Saturday Dad, Mark, and my big brother George helped me. Every day when I got home from school I worked on my game."

"Could you help me?" asked Pete.

"If you are willing to try," Jerry answered. "It takes time and hard work. Maybe we can get George to help us."

"When do we start?" Pete asked.

"Right now," Jerry laughed. "When once you have decided what you should do, the time to get busy is right now."

The Home Run

"Saturday is the best day of the week," Pete decided as he jumped out of bed and ran to the window. The morning was nice and sunny.

"Mother, is breakfast ready?" Pete called. "I don't want to be late."

Every Saturday for the last four weeks, Jerry, Mark, and Pete had played baseball in the lot next to Mr. Hill's house.

As soon as breakfast was over, Pete raced from the house. When he got to the lot, he saw his friends playing catch.

"Hurry up!" Jerry called. "Pete, you bat. Mark, you play field."

Pete took the bat and got ready.

"Pete, you'd better move back," Jerry said. "If you make a big hit, the ball might go through Mr. Hill's window."

"Oh, Pete can't hit the side of a barn!" laughed Mark.

"I can, too!" Pete cried. But he didn't really mean what he was saying.

"Ready?" Jerry called. Then a fast ball went flying down to Pete.

Pete hit the ball with everything he had, and it went flying off to left field. Mark ran after it as hard as he could go.

"It's a home run!" Jerry shouted.

The ball was going, going, going! Suddenly the boys heard it hit glass.

"Now you've done it!" Mark cried.

"But I really didn't think I could hit that far," said Pete.

"But you did!" Mark answered.

"Here comes Mr. Hill. Now we will catch it!" Jerry said.

"Let's get out of here," Mark shouted. He raced across the lot and down the block toward home.

"Jerry, should we—?" Pete started to ask. But Jerry was running, too.

"Wait!" Mr. Hill cried. "Wait for a second. The glass in my window has been——" But Pete was running, too.

When he came to his block, he slowed down.

"If Mother sees me running like this, she will be sure to know something's happened," he thought.

Pete walked across his yard and sat down on the steps to rest. "There's nothing good about this Saturday," he thought. "I wonder if Mr. Hill knows who we are? I hope Dad never finds out."

Just then the door opened and his mother stepped onto the steps. "Hi," she said. "Why are you home so early?"

"We couldn't play very long," he said.

"Then maybe you might like to go to the store with me," his mother asked.

"I think I'll just stay here," Pete answered, kicking at the steps with the back of one shoe.

Pete heard the car pull away. "Why didn't I tell Mother?" he asked himself. "And why did I run in the first place? Because I was scared, that's why. Now what am I to do about all this? Sister says that when we don't know what to do, we should sit down and think about what Jesus would have done."

Pete thought for a while as he sat kicking the steps. Then he said, "It's hard to decide. What **would** Jesus have done?"

He got up and started down the block. As he came near the baseball lot, he saw Mark and Jerry coming toward him.

"Hello, there!" Pete called, trying to pretend that everything was all right. "Where are you two going?"

"Could we all be going to the same place?" Jerry asked. Then the three boys began to laugh.

Pete gave each of his friends a pat on the back. "What are we waiting for?" he asked. "Let's go!"

The boys walked across the lot and up to Mr. Hill's back porch. Just as Jerry reached out to push the doorbell, Mr. Hill opened the door to the porch.

"Hi," said Mr. Hill. "I thought you would be coming."

"What do you mean?" Pete asked.

"I think I know you boys around here pretty well," Mr. Hill answered. "Now we'd better have a little talk about some glass. It looks as if you will be having some work to do for a lot of Saturdays to come."

The Party

One day Mary Ann came to school with a big cake, and Sister let her have a party. The next day the children were talking about the wonderful time they'd had.

"I am having a birthday soon," said Tony. "It comes on a Saturday. My party is going to last all day."

"My birthday comes in two weeks," said Katy. "My mother told me I could ask as many girls as I wanted."

"I never have a party," Mark said sadly. "My birthday comes early in the summer. That's when we always go on our trip."

Just then the bell began to ring, and the children had to go in.

Carlos thought all day long about what Mark had said. After school he stayed and talked to Sister Mary Jean. Then he went home and talked to his mother.

A week went by. Then one day, just before it was time to go home, Sister called Mark to the back of the room.

"Mark, will you please carry these books down to Miss Day in Room 103?" she asked. "And please clean Miss Day's boards for her while you are down there."

After Mark had left, Carlos' mother came in, carrying a big box of things. Everyone hurried to put them where they were to go. Then Sister Mary Jean stayed near the door to watch for Mark.

"Here he comes!" she whispered.

"Hurry! Hurry!" Carlos' mother whispered to the children.

The children and Carlos' mother went to a corner at the back of the room. They hurried so that Mark would not see them as he came in. And each pretended to be a little mouse.

Sister Mary Jean sat down at a table and was busy marking papers by the time Mark reached the door.

As Mark came in, the children raced out of the corner. "Happy Saint's Day to you!" they sang. "Surprise! Surprise!"

"Saint's Day?" Mark asked.

"Well, your name is Mark, isn't it?" Carlos smiled.

"Sure," answered Mark.

"Well, today is Saint Mark's Day," Carlos went on. "In my family we don't have birthday parties. But we do have a party on our Saint's Day. You can't have your birthday party this summer, so we decided to give you a Saint's Day party in its place."

Mark was too surprised to talk. He just went over to the table and looked. Higher than he could reach, there was a gray paper donkey with red ears. He looked so nice that Mark wanted to pat him.

"There's your gift from me," Carlos said, looking toward the hanging donkey.

"A paper donkey?" Mark asked.

"No," Carlos laughed. "Your gift from me is inside the donkey."

"But I can't reach him," Mark cried.

"You don't have to," Carlos replied. He put a long stick in Mark's hands. "Now pretend that this stick is a baseball bat and the donkey is a ball," he said.

"You will need this," Carlos' mother whispered. She handed Carlos a big pink handkerchief.

Carlos laughed, "Oh, yes. Come here, Mark. I'll have to tie this over your eyes.

"Ready now?" Carlos said. "One, two, and three. Everybody duck!"

Swish! Mark missed.

Swish, swish, SWISH! Mark hit at the hanging donkey again and again.

"You haven't hit it at all!" Tony called. "Move over a little."

Swish, swish, swish, BANG! Gifts came raining down all over the floor.

Mark pulled the pink handkerchief from his face. "This is a wonderful party!" he cried.

The children helped him pick up his gifts from the floor. Then they played some games that Carlos showed them.

Next they ate some nuts and some little cakes that Carlos' mother had made in her kind of way. As they ate, each told about his Saint's Day.

"My Saint's Day comes on the first of May," Jim Ball said.

"I have two Saint's Days," Mary Ann pointed out. "One is for the Blessed Mother, and one is for Saint Ann."

"We all do," Tony replied. "We all have second names, only lots of us don't get called by them as you do."

"I can't wait to tell my family about all the things you brought," said Mark.

"We're glad you're happy," said Sister Mary Jean.

"My family will be happy, too," Mark pointed out. "We are seven. There are George, Jerry, Ellen, Tommy, Mother, Dad, and me. That makes two times seven. Just think of all the parties **that** can be! Thank you so much for telling me about my Saint's Day."

The Mystery

One day Mary Ann, Susan Gray, and Tony were walking together. The girls asked Tony what he liked best, and he answered, "A mystery!"

Just then they saw a little boy. He was sitting on the sidewalk crying.

"Why is he crying?" Mary Ann asked.

Susan hurried to the little boy. "Are you hurt?" she said.

The boy didn't answer. Tony got down and looked him over with care. "I don't see any marks on him," Tony said.

The little boy looked up. His eyes were red, and his face was all wet and pink. "Home," he cried. He put his hands over his face and cried so hard that he shook all over.

"A mystery!" cried Tony. "A mystery for me to work on!"

"This isn't the time for working on a mystery," Susan pointed out. "This is the time for being a good Samaritan. We have to do something to help this boy."

"Let me ask some questions," Tony said. He put his hand on the boy's head. "Where do you live, little man?"

"Home," the little boy cried.

"That didn't get me anywhere," Tony said. "Little boy, what's your name?"

"Home," said the little boy.

"This really is a mystery!" cried Tony. "I think I'd better take some notes." He opened his notebook and put some notes down on a paper.

"Well, where is home, young man?" Tony asked. But the little boy just cried harder than ever.

"This is some mystery!" Tony cried. "I must make more notes." For a time he was busy as he wrote on his paper.

"Tony!" Mary Ann cried. "You're not being a good Samaritan. You're making a game out of this." She looked around and thought very hard.

"He can't have come far," she said. "He might know his home if he sees it."

She and Susan took the boy's hands and took him up and down the street. Tony walked behind, making notes as hard as he could. Once the boy sat down and wouldn't move. When Tony tried to help, he kicked at Tony's legs. Tony wrote down some notes about that, too.

Then Tony tried to play pony with the boy. And he asked more questions. But always he got the same answer. **Home.**

"Let's go back to our starting point," Susan said. "Perhaps it will help this young man remember something."

When they got there, Mary Ann saw something she didn't remember seeing before. It was a gate, and it was open.

"Do you think—?" Mary Ann began.

"Yes," said Susan. They went through the gate and up the porch steps.

A gray-haired woman came out. "Oh, Francis," she cried. "Where have you been?"

"He's been with us," Susan said. "We found him out here crying. He was so unhappy we thought he was lost. We were trying to find his home."

"Thank you," the woman said. "His mother brought him here to stay with his grandfather and me all night. Francis is always unhappy at first. He misses his mother. He will be better soon."

The three started for home together.

"Well, that takes care of the mystery of the lost boy," Tony said. "I really did some good work on that one."

"You?" Susan cried. "Who thought of coming back here in the first place?"

"You," said Tony, looking at his feet.

"Who saw a gate open and remembered what it might mean?" asked Mary Ann.

"You," Tony replied, still looking at his feet. Then he laughed, "But you can't say that I didn't ask a lot of very good questions!"

The Wooden Fence

"Can you see your dad, Steve?" asked Mark Winters.

"Not now," replied Steve Young. "My dad runs the biggest shovel behind this wooden fence. But we can't see him work from here."

Mark cried, "Say, Steve! There must be a gate somewhere for the machines to go through. We can't see much from here, but we could see through an open gate. Let's find a gate!"

Steve and Mark got up and ran around a corner. Then they saw a gate and a watchman standing by it.

The boys ran toward the gate. Just as they got there, a truck rolled out.

The watchman waved the big truck on through the gate.

Then he turned to Steve and Mark and said, "Sorry, boys. You'll be in the way here. Trucks go in and out this gate all day long."

"We wanted to watch my dad work," said Steve. "He runs the biggest shovel behind that fence."

The watchman said, "You must mean Big Steve Young."

Just then a truck rolled up outside the gate. Then another and another.

While the watchman was showing the trucks where to go, the boys turned and walked back around the high fence.

Soon they saw a box near the fence. "Let's stand on that box and try to look over the fence," said Steve.

He got up on the box and tried to reach the top of the fence to pull himself up. But he couldn't reach it.

As Steve jumped down, both boys saw the watchman hurrying toward them.

The watchman waved and called, "I've been looking for you boys. I want to help you see Big Steve."

The man walked to the wooden fence and began to cut a hole.

In a second, Steve said, "I know what you're doing! You're making a hole in the fence for us to look through!"

The watchman said, "I'm not done yet. I'm going to make two holes. We have to have two holes for two boys to look through."

The holes in the fence were placed just right—not too high and not too low. The boys could look through them and see everything that was happening.

Steve shouted, "There's my dad! He's running the biggest shovel."

Mark cried, "I see him!"

The boys watched for a long time. At last Steve said, "We'd better go home now, Mark. Dad will be surprised when he knows I saw him work today! I can't wait to tell him."

That night Steve said to his father, "I saw you work today. Mark did, too.

"We tried to look under the fence, but it was too near the ground. We tried to look over the fence, but we didn't have anything high enough to stand on. We couldn't reach the top.

"Then a friendly watchman came along and cut two holes in part of the wooden fence for us. The holes were just right—not too high and not too low. Mark and I saw everything then. We could see through the high wooden fence just fine!"

The Missionary

"This is Father Brown," Sister Mary Jean said. "Father is a missionary."

"Good morning," Father smiled. "Who knows anything about a missionary?"

David waved his hand. "All right, young man. You tell us," said Father.

"When a man is a missionary, he goes to a faraway country," David said. "I'm David. When I'm big, I'm going to be a missionary. I think it will be fun."

"A missionary must work very hard for God," said Father. "Will you do that?"

"What would I have to do?" said David.

"Let me tell you of my work," Father replied. "When I came to the country where I was to be a missionary, I had to build a church. Some of the farmers cut down trees for me. Others made the trees into boards and nailed them together for the first part of the building.

"These men soon had to leave to get back to their farming. The only one who could stay and help me was a young boy. I will call him John. You couldn't say his right name anyway.

"John was a very friendly boy, and he was a good worker. He could nail boards together as well as any man.

"It took us about a year to build our new church. We called it Saint Joseph's Church. It is not very big, yet Our Blessed Lord is there.

"John loved Our Blessed Lord very much. Each morning he walked to the church for Mass and Communion.

"One morning after Mass, a man came running and told John to hurry to his father's home. He said the river was suddenly getting higher and higher.

"When John got there, the river's rolling waters reached from hill to hill. John's family was gone, and he never saw them again. Later, a farmer who knew John took him to be his son.

"John was good at nailing boards, but he had never been to school," Father said. "He never even knew about schools."

Carlos smiled. "Would you like not going to school?" Father asked Carlos.

Carlos looked at the floor. "Don't you like to read?" Father asked.

"Carlos does very well when he tries," Sister said.

"John hadn't even seen a book until I gave him one," Father went on. "One day he came to me, carrying the book."

" 'What's this picture?' he asked.

" 'That is something to hold the waters of a river back,' I told him.

" 'If we could build something like that, then the river could never come up again, could it?' John asked.

" 'John, we can build a church, but we can't build that. We would have to read many books. It would be a long time before we would even know how to start.'

"John was very quiet for a while. Then he said, 'Father, someday I'm going to find a way to hold the river back. Even if I have to read every book in the world.'

"Then I knew we needed a school. So we started work on the building.

"Two weeks before I left to come here to visit my family, some sisters came to teach in our school. We have teachers now, but we need books to teach from."

Carlos smiled. "Father, you can have some of my books for your school."

"Our children could not read your books," Father said. "They can read only books that are for their country."

"If we only had money!" Susan said.

"Mr. Swan will buy old papers," David cried. "We could pick up newspapers from all the homes in the neighborhood."

Father Brown smiled. "David, I think you are a real missionary right now. If you others are willing to help, you too will be doing real missionary work. And please pray for us, won't you?"

"We must remember to pray for Father and his people every day," Sister said.

"We will," cried Carlos. "Whenever we go to Mass and Communion, we will ask Our Blessed Lord to help everyone at your Saint Joseph's Church."

Poor Me

One Saturday afternoon Katy Burns came into the kitchen to get her bank.

Mrs. Burns looked at the bank sitting on top of the kitchen icebox. "Katy," she said, "last week you told me never to give you that bank. Remember?"

Katy looked down at the floor.

"You said that you were keeping your money for Saint Joseph's School," Mrs. Burns went on. "You won't have enough if I don't keep you from taking it out of the bank."

"I know," Katy said. "But just this once won't hurt. I want to go to the show with Linda and Susan. Please, Mother. I need a dime. I have the rest."

Mrs. Burns gave Katy an unhappy look. "All right," she said. "I'll give you the bank. But, poor John."

"What do you mean by 'poor John'?" Katy asked.

"He'll never have books if you keep taking money from your bank," Mrs. Burns replied. "What will poor John do?"

Katy didn't say anything. She just looked at the bank. Now and then Mrs. Burns would look at her quiet little girl and say, "Poor John."

At last Katy faced her mother and said, "You're right. I'll never save any money for Saint Joseph's School if I keep taking dimes from the bank whenever I want to. I have decided that I won't go to the show today."

Three Saturdays later, Katy came running into the kitchen again. "May I go to the show this afternoon?" she asked. "Linda is waiting at the bus stop."

"Yes, if you have the money," Mrs. Burns replied.

"I'll get some from my bank," Katy called as she raced to her bedroom.

Mrs. Burns turned toward the icebox. There sat Katy's bank that looked like a bus. "Katy," Mrs. Burns called, "your bank is here in the kitchen."

"I have some money for myself in here," Katy shouted back.

Katy ran back to the kitchen and began to shake her blue bank that looked like an egg. Two dimes rolled across the floor. She gave the egg another shake. Five pennies and a dime came out.

"Where did you get that?" Mrs. Burns asked. "I've never seen it before."

"Mr. Hill gave it to me when I helped clean his yard," Katy answered.

"Poor John," Mrs. Burns said. "Now you're just saving money for yourself."

"Oh, no," Katy cried. "Not just for myself. Some of the money I get each week goes in the bus bank. The rest goes in my egg bank. The money I save in the bus bank is for poor John. The money in the egg bank is for **poor me.**"

The Best Worker

Every school day the boys and girls in Room 207 had been going to Mass and Communion to pray for Father Brown's missionary work. They opened each day by praying to Our Blessed Lord for Father's school.

One morning after the children had prayed, Sister Mary Jean said, "I think we should write to Father Brown. It would be nice to write him a friendly letter about what we have been doing to make money these last eight weeks."

"I want to write him about how I do baby-sitting each week," said Katy.

"I want to write about the dimes I saved when I helped Dad," said Joseph.

"I cared for my uncle's pets and saved my money," said Tim.

"We mustn't forget to write about our paper drive on Saturday," Sister said.

"Sister," Billy asked, "could we make a game out of the drive? Mark thinks he can get more papers than anyone else."

"Fine," the teacher replied. "I'll get a surprise gift for the best worker."

On Saturday everyone met after the eight o'clock Mass. There were bikes, carts, wagons, and boxes everywhere in the schoolyard. Each of the children was sure he could be the best worker.

Sister Mary Jean made markers and wrote the names of the children on them. Father Parks put sticks into the ground and nailed the markers into place.

Then Father nailed up a large wooden marker. He wrote on it, "Please help a missionary! Give us your old papers."

"Let's get started," Father said.

"Please wait a minute," Billy March cried. "I have to oil the wheels on David's wagon."

Just then Mark Winters came running up. "Sorry I'm late," he puffed. "I had to hurry home and get something ready before I could meet you."

"Where's your cart?" Joseph asked.

Mark just smiled and stayed quiet.

"The drive ends at three o'clock," Father said. "We'll meet here."

About two in the afternoon, Billy and Joseph stopped in the schoolyard to rest. "Mark has three times as many papers as anyone else," Billy said. "What kind of cart is he using?"

"He must have a truck," Joseph said. "The ground is filled near his marker."

"I'm tired!" Joseph cried.

"I'll oil the wheels on your wagon," Billy said. "Maybe they'll work easier." He got down on the ground and started to oil the wagon's wheels.

"Look!" Joseph cried. "Here comes Mark."

Billy dropped the oil can and got to his feet. "Oh, no!" he cried. "Only Mark would think of something as handy as that cart is."

Mark ran to his marker. Behind him came Tramp, pulling the filled cart. Mark stopped the dog and began throwing the papers out.

When Mark was through throwing his papers on the ground, he looked up and saw Billy and Joseph. "You look tired," he called.

"We've been working like dogs," Joseph answered. "It must be handy to have a real dog pull your cart."

Mark patted Tramp and said, "Yes, it is. Come, Tramp. We've more work to do."

The two tired boys watched Mark and Tramp go down the street. "I've just thought of something," Billy grinned. "Come on. Let's go talk to Sister."

The first school morning after the paper drive, Billy and Joseph carried a box into Sister's room and put it on her table. When the children had prayed, Sister pointed to the box.

"Here's the gift for the best worker," she said. "Mark, come up and get it."

Mark came, grinning all the way. Sister gave him the box. "Open it," she said. She and a few others put their hands over their mouths to hide their smiles.

Mark found a note on top that said, "For the best worker in the paper drive. This box is filled with something to eat."

Mark's mouth dropped as he opened the box. "Eight cans of dog food!" he cried.

"Well," Sister laughed, "Tramp was the best worker, wasn't she?"

Who Owns This Hat?

"A real fireman's hat!" shouted Pat Gray. "I'll keep it! I can have a lot of fun playing fireman with this hat."

"It's my hat, too!" cried Bill Stone. "We were right together, and we saw it at the same time. You just picked it up before I could get it."

Bill tried to pull the hat out of Pat's hands, but Pat held on to it.

"Let go of my hat!" shouted Pat.

Bill would not give up his hold.

Just then Mark Winters' oldest brother, George, came running up to them. He said to the two younger boys, "What's all the shouting about? What happened?"

Pat said, "Bill is trying to take my hat. It's no toy. It's a real city fireman's hat. I found it a minute ago."

"I found it at the same time he did," Bill cried. "So it's my hat, too."

"All right!" said George. "Now listen to me for a few minutes, boys. One of our city firemen lost that hat. Did you see a fire engine go past that corner?"

Bill said, "We didn't really see a fire engine, but we thought we heard one a little while ago."

"The man who lost that hat will have to buy another one," said George. "All the firemen in our city have to buy their own hats. I'm sure it takes lots of money to buy a fireman's hat."

The two younger boys began to feel unhappy as they listened to George.

At last Pat turned to Bill and said in a friendly way, "I think we should try to find out who owns this hat."

"I think so myself," said Bill. "I hope the owner of that hat is at the firehouse on Green Street."

Pat said, "Let's go there together this afternoon and take the hat."

That afternoon Pat and Bill went to the firehouse. It was a brick building, and in front of it were three firemen, washing one of the fire engines.

Pat held up the hat. "My friend and I found this on Spring Road and brought it here. It's a real fireman's hat. Does anyone here own it? I hope so."

One man called to someone inside the brick building. "Step out here, Red."

A friendly young fireman with red hair came out. He looked pleased when he saw what the boys were carrying.

"That's my hat!" he cried. "I hoped someone would find it. I got that hat almost ten years ago. I was hoping that I wouldn't have to buy a new one. Thanks for bringing it to me."

He shook hands with Pat and Bill. "Maybe you two would like to know how it feels to be a fireman?" he asked.

"Oh, yes," the boys cried together.

The boys sat on a real fire engine and pretended they were going across the city to a big fire. They pretended to ring the bell. They pretended to hurry around corners on two wheels. They pretended they were driving as fast as the wind.

When at last they had to go, they went to Red and the rest of the firemen and told them good-by.

Red called, "Be sure to come and visit us again this summer, boys."

Pat grinned, "We'll keep our eyes open for lost hats, too."

What Pete Found Out

"Hi, Pete!" said Pat Gray. "Jim Ball and I are going to the city pool to swim. Do you want to go with us?"

Pete wished he could say, "Sure! Sure I'll go with you. I'll swim across that pool faster than anyone."

But Pete was afraid of the water. So all he said was, "I have something to do uptown. See you later!"

Then he raced off toward town.

When Pete reached town, he walked along looking in all the store windows. He said to himself, "A fine summer I'm going to have if all my friends go to the pool every day of the week!"

Pete saw Mr. Ball sitting inside his clock store. He was working on a clock that Pete's aunt had brought in. Pete liked Mr. Ball. So he went in to see him.

"Glad to see you," said Mr. Ball. He could tell that Pete was unhappy, but he said nothing about it.

He went on working on the clock. Pete watched him work.

Before long Pete said, "Mr. Ball, have you ever wanted to do something but you couldn't make yourself do it?"

"Yes, Pete," replied Mr. Ball. "That has happened to everyone."

Pete said, "I mean something easy that everybody can do. Like——"

"Like what, Pete?" asked Mr. Ball.

"Like swimming!" said Pete. "I know how to move my arms and legs the right way. I could do that last summer. I want to jump into the pool, stick my face in the water, and swim the way my friends do. But I just can't do it. I'm afraid."

Mr. Ball gave Pete a friendly smile. "Maybe I can help you," he said.

He put the clock down and began to look for something. Soon he handed a penny to Pete. It was almost like other pennies, but it was bigger.

"Perhaps this lucky penny is what you need, Pete," said Mr. Ball.

Mr. Ball told Pete all about the penny. "Long ago, people used pennies like this to buy things," he said. "This one has been a good-luck penny for many years. My grandfather and my father carried it. They thought it brought them luck.

"I'm going to let you carry it, Pete. Maybe it will bring you luck, too."

Pete asked, "Do you mean I'll be lucky enough to swim if I carry it?"

Mr. Ball said, "Maybe you will, Pete. I hope so. And if you are really lucky, you'll find out something."

Pete thanked Mr. Ball and ran home with the penny. He put it in the pocket of his new red swimming trunks.

"I'm glad Aunt Jean gave me these new trunks last week," he said to himself. "My old red trunks don't have a pocket."

At first Pete thought that he would go right to the pool and try the lucky penny. Then he decided to go early the next day.

Pete got to the city pool very early the next morning. His friends were not there. But he saw high-school boys swimming at the deep end of the pool.

George Winters waved to Pete and began to swim across the pool.

Pete watched him and thought, "How easy swimming looks when George does it! I hope it will be that easy for me now that I have my lucky penny."

Pete made sure the lucky penny was in his pocket. Then he began to slide into the water. It was cold, but it was not very deep.

He held on to the side of the pool with both hands and kicked his feet. Next he turned sideways and faced the deep end of the pool. He held on with just one hand, kicked his feet, and moved one arm in the water.

He heard George call from the deep end, "Pete, you are almost swimming."

Soon Pete started to move both arms and kick. "I'm swimming!" he thought. "The lucky penny did it! Maybe I can open my eyes under water, too."

He tried and found that he could. Then he began swimming again.

In a short while, Pete left the pool and went to see Mr. Ball at the clock store. "You were right, Mr. Ball," said Pete. "That lucky penny did it! I can swim with it in my pocket."

When Pete saw Jim and Pat going to the pool the next day, he called, "Wait for me! I'm going swimming."

He ran to get his new trunks. Then he remembered that he had not put them outside to dry. So he put his old trunks under his arm, and off he ran.

At the pool the boys got ready as fast as they could and raced to the water.

Pat jumped in first. Pete jumped into the water right behind him.

Down went Pete. For just a second he thought that he would never come up. But up he came. Then he kicked and splashed to the side of the pool. It was only a short way, but he was swimming.

Pete wanted to show the lucky penny to the boys. He reached for his pocket. But there was no pocket in his trunks! These were his old ones. The new ones were at home, and so was the penny.

Pete was scared for a second because he had been swimming without the penny. Then he laughed and began to swim again.

Later that day Pete took the penny to Mr. Ball at the clock store. "Thanks for letting me carry it," said Pete. "At first I thought that I couldn't swim without the penny to help me. But then I was really lucky. I found out that I don't need the penny. I can swim without it.

"This is going to be a fine summer!"

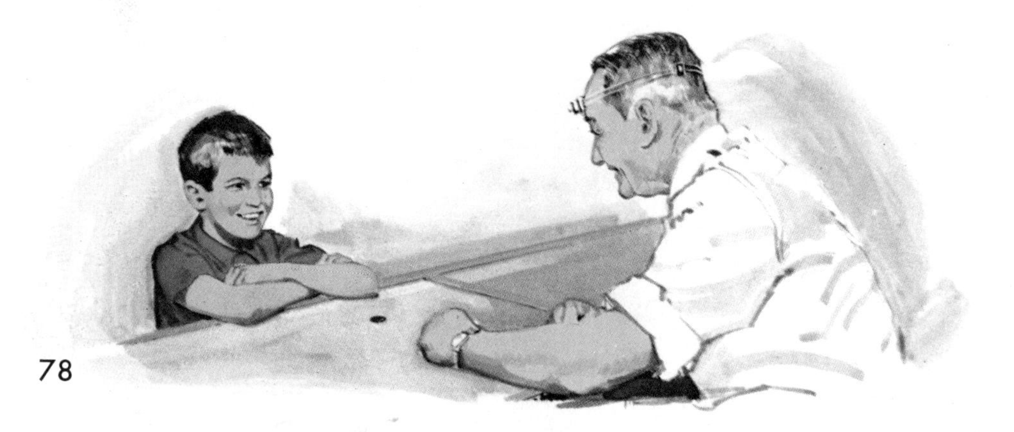

Saints for a Day

"George!" Mark called. He and his friends raced up to talk to George, who was sitting with Jerry on the porch steps.

"Guess what!" Katy cried. "We're to take part in the city's Flag Day Parade."

"Dad is letting the school use his truck," Mark went on. "We're all to be dressed up, and the truck will have a big picture of the world on it. On the way back, our truck is to go past Mr. Hill's house. We can do this only if you drive."

"I think I can find the time," George said. "What are you going to dress as?"

"As saints," Katy said.

"Saints!" George laughed. "You all may be dressed as saints, but you're no more saints than——"

"Than you are!" David said with a grin.

George looked at David in surprise. First his face turned pink and then red. "I certainly didn't mean——" he began.

"Why, George," Katy laughed. "A boy as old as you are couldn't help being ready to be made a saint. You have had so many more years to pray and be good than we have."

"I can see it now," David shouted. "**Saint** George Winters!"

"Stop it!" George cried. "This isn't funny. We all want to be saints someday. That is why God made us. But it takes more than dress-up clothes to make a saint. We have to **try** to be one. I'm trying. And you should try harder.

"Come, Jerry," George went on. "We haven't cleaned Dad's car yet. He wants it ready for his trip tomorrow."

The two boys went down the steps and around the house. As they left, George laughed and said, "Saints!"

"Sister said anyone who tried could be a saint," Katy said. "Even you, Carlos. You know how you put off doing things."

"I wish I knew what it would take to make a saint out of me," said Pat Gray. "I'm not bad much of the time."

"Sister says saints do hard things for the love of God," Carlos said. "We could try that. Jesus would help us."

"That's interesting," Mark said. "Now, what's the hardest thing for me to do?"

"To let the rest of us have our own way once in a while," Joseph cried.

"All right," Mark answered. "And I'll do everything I'm told to do, too."

"I won't make fun of people any more," Katy said. "I hurt their feelings."

"I will think before I open my mouth," David said. "I shouldn't laugh at other people. I wasn't nice to George."

"I'll do all my schoolwork on time," Carlos said. "I'll have my homework done when I get to school tomorrow."

"I won't feel sorry for myself when Dad says I can't go somewhere," Pat said.

"I'll go to Mass this summer as many times as I can," Mary Ann cried.

"We should all be well on our way toward being saints by the time that the Flag Day Parade comes," Carlos said.

A few weeks later, the children came to the school playground dressed in the parade clothes. But they looked very sad.

"You certainly are sad-looking saints," Father Parks cried. "Things surely can't be that bad. Jesus' saints are always happy. Come now. What's the trouble?"

"It's hard to be a saint," Carlos said. "We've worked and worked ever since we decided that if we were going to dress like saints in the Flag Day Parade, we must be like them in every way."

"So that's it!" Sister Mary Jean cried. "I am finally finding out why you had your homework done every day. And why Mark was so easy to get along with."

"Your wish to be like the saints is very interesting," Father said. "But what's the trouble? Why are you so sad?"

"I did my homework each night," Carlos said, kicking at a stone. "But Mother says that just doing homework isn't enough. I must come when she calls, do what my father asks, and try to be good all the time. And that's just a **start!** Oh, Father, I'll never be a saint!"

Mark could feel his ears getting red. "I gave in to everybody for almost two weeks," he said. "But now I'm back to telling everyone what to do."

"I forgot everything this morning," David said sadly. "I talked back to my mother. She said that since I was bad, I couldn't be in the parade this afternoon. When you go past Mr. Hill's house, please wave at him for me."

"Mary Ann has been going to Mass every day," Katy cried. "She's the only one who has done what she said she would."

"The summer has just started," Mary Ann said. "I have a long way to go."

"The road to being good is not easy," Father Parks said. "I can see why you're sad. But you really shouldn't feel that way. Each of you wants to be one of God's saints, and each of you did make a good start. What you must remember is this: **never stop trying!**"

"It's time for this Flag Day Parade to start moving!" George yelled as he ran up to the truck.

"If you're driving, I think we had better walk!" Katy yelled back. And she laughed at how funny she was. Then she remembered Father Parks' words.

"Oh, dear," she said to herself. "It's always time for **me** to keep on trying!"

I Like It Here

When the downtown part of the city Flag Day Parade was over, the children in Room 207 came together at the Winters' truck. On the way back to the school, they were to go past Mr. Hill's house.

"Let's go," Mark yelled. "Bill, hold that flag higher. And smile! We're supposed to look happy for Mr. Hill."

The crowd of children paraded down the street. Soon they reached Mr. Hill's block and paraded past his house.

"This is the best Flag Day Parade I've ever seen," said Mr. Hill. "Now I have a surprise for you. Come."

Mr. Hill led the children around the house to his back porch. There they saw a table filled with good food.

"Oh, Mr. Hill!" Tony cried. "This is surely a wonderful surprise."

The children ate, then played games. Everyone was having a good time. That is, everyone but Bill Stone. He just sat and watched the other children play.

Finally Mr. Hill called from his rocking chair. "Come here, Bill. Come and tell me what's troubling you."

"At breakfast today my father told me that we're moving away," Bill said. "I won't be with my friends any more."

Just then Pete and Pat yelled, "Hi, Bill! We want to play baseball. Come on." But Bill just shook his head.

"Why does he look so sad?" Pete asked.

"Let's find out," Pat replied. He led the other boys across the yard, and they crowded around the rocking chair.

"Bill has bad news," Mr. Hill said. "His family is moving away."

"Where are you going?" Patty asked.

"I forgot the name of the place," Bill answered. "It's so far from here that we'll have to drive for four days just to get there."

"Think of the places you'll see!" said Mr. Hill. "This is a huge country."

"I don't want to go," Bill cried. "I like it here. I begged and begged, but we're still going to move."

"Now, Bill, your father's work is taking him away," Mr. Hill said. "There is nothing he can do about that."

"I suppose you're right," Bill replied.

"You've never seen much of our country," Mr. Hill went on. "You don't know how wonderful it is. Why, I've seen places that made me wonder how God could have made anything so beautiful."

"Tell us," the children begged.

"I've seen a place that looked as if God Himself had cut the face of the earth open," said Mr. Hill. "Deep in the earth ran a river, past rocks more huge than any you've seen. They looked as if God had used every color on earth to paint them.

"I saw cities with buildings so high you would think they could make holes in the sky. I saw fields so green I wanted to reach out and pat them."

"I certainly would like to see places like that," Linda Long said.

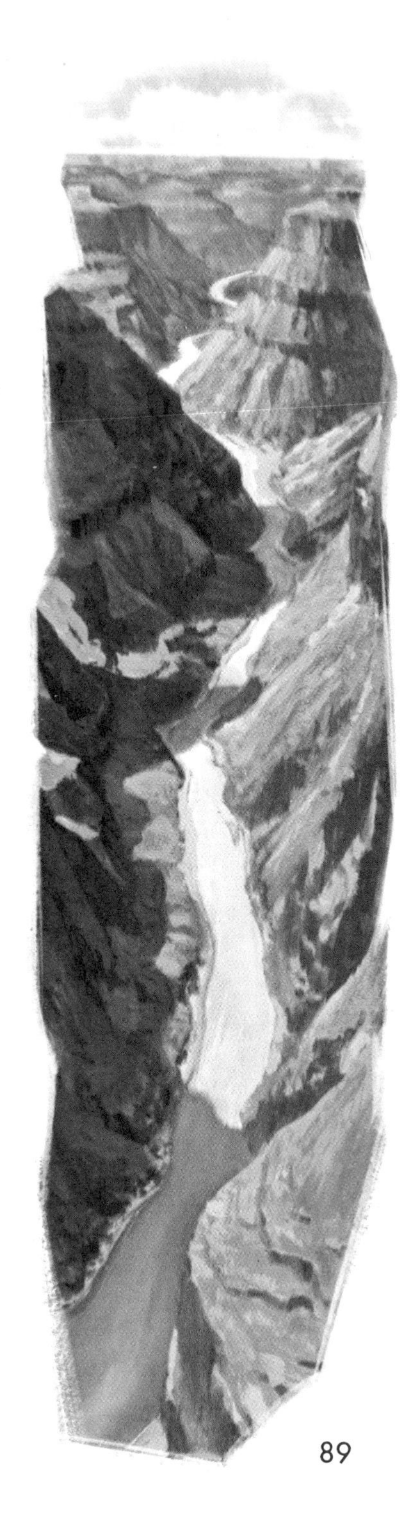

"You wouldn't if it was going to mean that you would never see your friends again," Bill replied slowly. For a minute he thought he was going to cry.

"Bill," Mark said, "when we got ready to move here last winter, I didn't want to leave my old neighborhood and friends. But look at all the new friends I've made since I came here."

"That's right, Bill," Mr. Hill smiled. "Why, in no time at all you'll be writing to tell us of all the nice things that are happening to you. The world is filled with interesting people to meet and know."

"I suppose you're right," Bill finally said. "I certainly hope so."

About four weeks later, Mr. Hill called Mark and asked him to bring his friends to Mr. Hill's house. When all were quiet, Mr. Hill opened a note and read the words that were on it.

Dear Mr. Hill,

You were right. I like it here. The neighborhood is filled with children. The family next door has seven. One boy, Jack, will be in my room at Saint John's School. He has taken me everywhere.

Last Saturday we went high up in the hills and made snowballs. The sky was blue like summer, but there was snow on the ground.

I wish all my old friends could meet all my new friends. There certainly would be a big crowd!

Bill

ANIMAL FRIENDS

A Good Name for a Dog

Steve Young had been downtown getting some gardening gloves for his mother. All the way home on the bus, he was busy thinking of his new puppy. It had been a birthday gift from his aunt and uncle.

When the bus stopped at his corner, Steve raced down the street. He just had to see his puppy. It was so new that he hadn't even named it yet.

He hurried across the grass and toward his back yard. Then he stopped. The gate was open. The puppy was gone!

"Mother!" Steve yelled. "Look here. My birthday puppy is gone!"

Mrs. Young hurried to the yard. "Oh!" she cried. "Someone forgot to hook the gate. You'd better find him at once."

Steve whistled and called, but the puppy didn't come. Then Steve handed the box with the gloves to his mother and raced down the street.

In the next block he saw Debbie Wills sitting on the grass. She had her chin in her hands, and she was crying.

"What's the trouble?" Steve called.

"A bad puppy has taken my best pink handkerchief," Debbie said. "I tied it under his chin and he ran off with it."

"Was he a friendly brown-and-white puppy with white feet?" Steve asked.

"He was," Debbie answered slowly.

"He's my new puppy!" Steve cried. "I'll track him down. When I find him, I'll bring you your pink handkerchief."

Steve ran down the next block. There he saw a newsboy picking up his papers.

"Hi!" Steve yelled excitedly. "Did you see a brown-and-white puppy?"

"I surely did," the newsboy replied. "He raced right in front of me. I had to turn my bike to miss him, and then my front wheel hit the wet grass."

Steve helped pick up the papers. In a few minutes they all were back in the bike basket where they belonged.

"Thanks," the boy called as he went riding off. "Your puppy went that way."

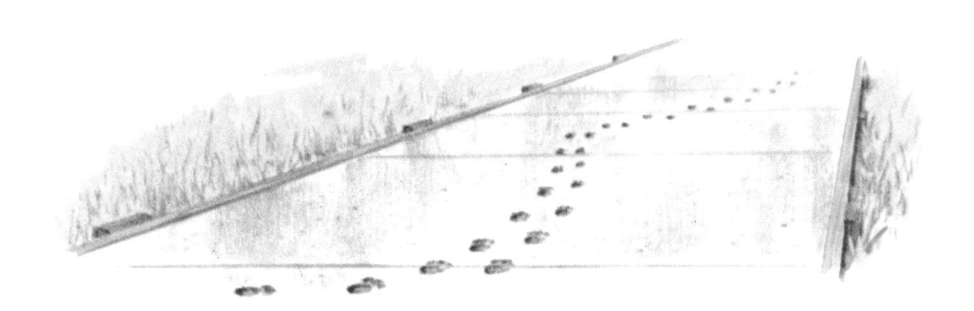

Steve ran to the corner. There he saw a new sidewalk with dog tracks on it. He ran along the grass and followed the tracks, which led down the block.

Soon Steve saw some people crowding around an oak tree at the corner. A few were looking up into the tree. Others were looking down at something.

Steve ran up. There he saw his puppy with a pink handkerchief tied under his chin. He was barking excitedly at a huge kite that was hanging from the oak tree.

"That's my puppy!" Steve cried.

A man in the crowd laughed. "I think your pup wants that kite. So do I. It belongs to my son. It looks as if I'll have to climb up in the oak and get it."

"I'll get the kite down," Steve said. He chinned himself on a low branch of the oak tree. Then he kicked his feet up and hooked his legs over the branch. He climbed to the next branch, but the kite was still out of reach. Then he climbed even higher. Finally he reached the kite and pulled it from the branches.

Steve dropped the kite to the boy's father. Then he climbed down, picked up his excited puppy, and hurried away.

On the way home, Steve gave Debbie the handkerchief his puppy had taken.

When he got to his back yard, Steve shut the gate and carefully hooked it. Then he and the dog ran to the kitchen.

"Mother, look!" Steve cried excitedly. "I followed my puppy's tracks and finally found him. Don't you think that 'Tracks' would be a good name for him?"

Steve's mother pointed to the tracks on the kitchen floor. "You are right," she said. "For that dog there couldn't be a better name!"

Who Did?

The school bus, carrying Father Parks, Sister Mary Jean, and the children of Room 207, rolled along the city streets and out into the country. Finally it turned down a side road and stopped at a big white farmhouse.

Two children waved from the porch and hurried down to meet the bus. "Hi!" they called excitedly.

When everyone was standing on the grass, Father Parks said, "I want you to know Nancy and Jack Banks. They moved to this farm a short time ago. They'll be coming to our school next fall."

"We're glad to meet you," Nancy and Jack smiled. "Come. Follow us to our little lake. We're to play near there." Then Nancy and Jack led the way.

Mrs. Banks came hurrying out of the house, followed by Mrs. Good. They were to take care of the food.

Katy did not go to the lake. "Mrs. Good, may I help you?" she begged.

"Yes," Mrs. Good replied. "Take the boxes of cookies out of this basket."

As Katy reached into the basket, she said, "I smell peanut butter cookies. Oh, Mrs. Good, your peanut butter cookies surely are the best in the world!"

"For those nice words, I think a hungry worker might have a cookie," Mrs. Good said. "Help yourself, dear."

As Katy put the boxes on the table, she ate the cookie Mrs. Good gave her. It was so good she took two more. One of them she ate. The other she put in her pocket. "For later," she thought.

Each time Katy went by the table, she took two more peanut butter cookies from the box. "One for now, and one for later," she kept telling herself.

While she was putting some glasses and straws around on the table, Linda Long came running up. "Katy, help me!" Linda cried excitedly. "Mark wants to put something funny in my hand."

"Linda!" Mark grinned. "It won't hurt you. Hold out your hand."

"I certainly will not!" Linda cried.

Katy put the glasses and straws on the table and held out her hand. "Here," she said. "Let's see what it is."

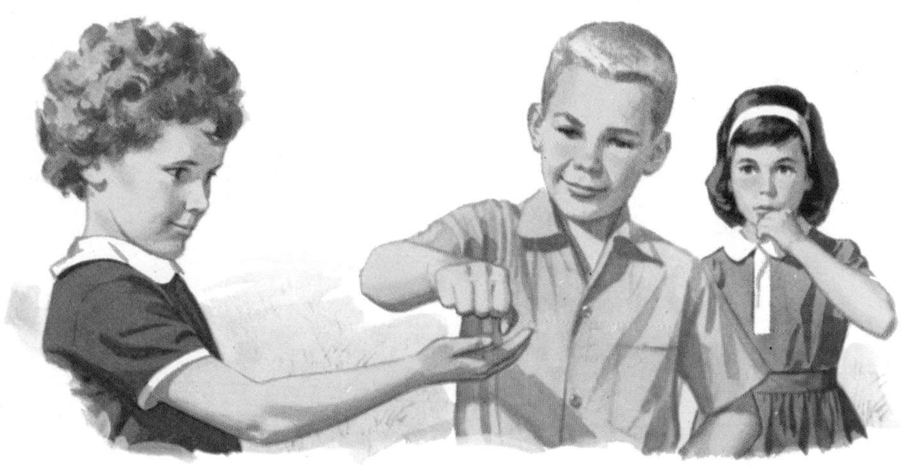

Mark carefully held his closed hand on Katy's open one. "When I let this thing fall, shut your hand," he said.

"I can feel something moving!" Katy cried and opened her hand a little. Just then a tiny living thing jumped out.

"I lost it!" Katy cried. "What was it?"

"I don't know," Mark answered. "We caught it down by the lake."

Just then Joseph ran up and took the box that Katy had been taking peanut butter cookies from. "There's nothing in this box," he said. "May I have it?"

"Yes," said Katy without looking.

"Hurry, Mark," Joseph cried. "Let's catch some more of those tiny things. I want to find out about them."

When lunch was ready, Mrs. Banks rang a handbell. Soon the hungry children were crowding around the table.

Suddenly Mrs. Good cried, "Where is our other box of peanut butter cookies?"

Just then Joseph came hurrying up from the lake. He had a box in his hands.

"There's the missing box!" Mrs. Good cried. "Do you have the cookies?"

Joseph put the box on the table near Katy. "There wasn't anything in this box when I took it," he said.

Father Parks said, "Well, let's eat. I'm sure that whoever took the peanut butter cookies will soon feel sorry and tell us about it." Then he began to pray, "Bless us, O Lord——"

"If I don't tell, no one will know," Katy thought. "I won't get caught."

Suddenly she heard a little voice say, "Katydid." She looked around, but no one was talking to her. The next minute she heard two, three, four voices. Finally there were so many voices she couldn't tell how many she was hearing. "Katydid, katydid, katydid," the voices kept saying over and over.

Katy covered her ears so that she wouldn't hear the voices. When she took her hands away, she heard them again.

"Oh," Katy thought, "the voices are coming from the cookie box." She was so scared she began to shake all over. She kept looking at the closed cookie box.

"Katydid, katydid," the voices said.

Katy took the cookies from her pockets and piled them on the table. "Yes, I did, I did!" she cried. "I'm bad. I took the cookies!" And she began to cry.

Sister Mary Jean hurried over to Katy. "Don't cry, dear," she said. "Don't cry."

"Oh, Sister," Katy said. "You told us that when we did something wrong, we would hear a small voice inside us. I must be very bad, for I hear many voices. They come from that cookie box, and they keep saying, 'Katydid!' Oh, Sister, I **did** take that pile of cookies. But I'm sorry. What I did was wrong."

Sister slowly picked up one corner of the box cover and carefully looked inside. "Oh, Katy," she laughed. "Do you know what I see in this box?"

Katy shook her head.

"I see katydids," said Sister. "They are an interesting kind of tiny animal, and all they can say is 'Katy did'!"

Tramp

Mr. Winters, his son Jerry, and Pat Gray stood watching Tramp and her seven puppies. The puppies were so young they didn't have their eyes open yet.

"Was Tramp that tiny when she was a puppy?" Pat asked in a low voice.

"I suppose so," Mr. Winters said. "I never saw Tramp when she was a puppy."

"You mean she was a big dog when you got her?" Pat asked.

Jerry grinned. "The way we got Tramp makes an interesting story," he said.

"It all began very early Christmas Day," Jerry went on. "We came home from Christmas Mass to find a dog sitting on our back porch. An icy wind was blowing, and the poor dog was shaking.

"Mark rushed into the house and got some food. Before he could give it to her, Dad stopped him. 'If you feed that tramp dog, she will never leave,' Dad said. 'We must send her on her way.'

"We begged and begged, but Dad wouldn't let us feed the dog. He quickly closed the door and told us to go to bed.

"But we couldn't sleep. We kept hearing the dog crying. The icy wind blew and blew and blew. We kept thinking of how unhappy the poor dog must be.

"Finally George said, 'I can't stand it!' He jumped out of bed, and we followed him toward the kitchen. We could see a river of light coming from under the closed door. Slowly George pushed the door open.

"There was Dad sitting near the table with some leftover roast nearby. At his feet sat the dog. Dad reached over and picked up some roast. The dog sat up and begged. Dad laughed and dropped some of the roast into the dog's mouth. Then he reached for more roast.

"We just stood there and laughed. When Dad heard us, he jumped up.

"'If you feed that tramp dog, she'll never leave,' George cried. Then Dad started to laugh, too. Soon the rest of the family was up, and we had a party for our new tramp dog."

The Day Before the Fair

Nancy and Jack Banks sat on the fence in front of their father's farm. It was the day before the fair, and the excited children were watching the trucks go by. These were filled with fat farm animals being taken to the fair.

Suddenly Nancy cried, "Jack! Look at those two ponies galloping up the road! I believe they got away from someone. I hope they stop before they get hurt."

When the ponies came closer, they did stop. Then they slowly began to eat the grass near the farm fence.

Jack looked carefully at both ponies. "I don't believe those ponies belong to any farmer around here," he said. "We had better get them off the highway."

"Let's coax them into our barnyard," said Nancy. "We can pen them up there."

"All right," said Jack. "You hold the gate open. I'll try to get them inside."

Nancy ran quickly to open the gate, while Jack walked carefully toward the ponies. He gave a low, coaxing whistle. The two animals looked up, but they did not come any closer to the boy. They just began eating grass again.

"Maybe I can coax them in if I offer them some corn," thought Jack.

He got corn from the barn and offered it to the ponies. But he still couldn't coax them into the barnyard.

Finally Nancy called, "Let's offer some apples to the ponies. I believe they'll come for apples. I'll go get some."

Nancy rushed back with some apples. "Come here," she coaxed, holding out an apple to each pony.

The two ponies lifted their heads. As they reached out to the good apple smell, Nancy coaxed them back toward the barnyard. Step by step the two ponies followed. Nancy kept on backing until they had followed her into the barnyard.

Soon a truck tooted at the gate. The driver waved and called, "I see someone caught my ponies. Was it you?"

"Yes," Nancy replied. "We knew they shouldn't be galloping up the highway."

"Thanks," said the man. "I was taking my ponies to the fair when I got a nail in a tire. While I was getting my tools out, a plane went overhead. The ponies got scared and kicked the tail gate down. I guess I hadn't closed it right. They galloped off before I could catch them. Now I'll put them back in the truck."

Nancy laughed, "I hope you get those ponies into your truck more easily than we coaxed them into our barnyard.

"My brother whistled to them, but they didn't move. Then he offered them some corn. Still they didn't move. Finally I offered them apples, and they followed me all the way inside."

"Good!" said the man. "I'm glad you thought of offering them apples. But there is a better way to make these ponies go where you want them to go."

The man walked to his truck and let down the tail gate. Then he came back to where the ponies stood. "Get up on the ponies," he said. "See how easily you can make them go into the truck."

Jack and his sister got a big surprise when they climbed on the ponies' backs. At once the two animals trotted out of the barnyard. Then they trotted into the back of the truck and stood there.

Jack and Nancy rode the ponies up into the truck with no trouble at all.

"Wasn't that easy?" asked the man as the children quickly got off the ponies.

"These animals give rides at fairs all over the country. Each pony is trained to start moving as soon as someone is on its back. I get a dime for each ride.

"Come to the fair tomorrow and have some free rides. You saved my ponies from getting hurt. So you may have all the free rides you want!"

Jim Goes Camping

One summer afternoon Jim Ball rode with his father to a big lake. It was Jim's birthday, and his father was taking him on a camping trip near his aunt's farm. They were going to fish all weekend.

Jim had fished once before. That time he had caught just one fish. It was so little that he had to throw it back. This time he hoped to get some big fish.

It was too late for fishing by the time their camp was ready. But Jim went to the lake to get some tiny fish for bait.

Jim came back with a pail filled with bait. He lifted the pail and showed the bait to his father.

"Well, son!" laughed Mr. Ball. "You will catch fish easily with all that. Now put the pail in the water close to the bank of the lake. Be sure to shut the cover and tie the pail to a tree."

Jim did as his father told him and was soon back at camp for the night.

Early the next morning Mr. Ball and Jim ate a good breakfast. Then the boy rushed down to the lake to get his bait. He grabbed the bait pail and swished his hand around inside. The bait was gone!

"That's strange," said Mr. Ball when Jim told him about the missing bait. "The people we meet around here are always very friendly. I don't believe any of them would have taken your bait. Did you hear anyone in the woods near our camp last night?"

"No, I didn't," replied Jim. "I was so tired that I went right to sleep.

"I'll get some more bait. Then we'll see what happens to it."

Jim easily caught some more tiny fish. The bait pail was still in the water near the bank of the lake. Jim left some of his bait in the pail. The rest of it he put in a can to use right away.

Mr. Ball and Jim fished all day long. Jim caught one fish in the morning, but it was so small he had to throw it back. In the afternoon he kept getting one fish after another. Mr. Ball took a picture of the excited boy holding up his fish.

When the sky got dark, Jim took his flashlight from the toolbox and looked all around the camp. Then he turned the light off and sat down near the bait pail.

It seemed a long, long time before Jim heard a strange noise close by. Quickly he flashed his light onto the sandy bank, but he could see nothing near the pail.

Jim turned his flashlight off again and kept on waiting in the dark. At first it seemed very quiet in the woods. Then suddenly he heard a small splash. He turned on his flashlight at once.

There in the light was a raccoon! The animal was lifting a fish out of the pail.

Jim's light didn't seem to trouble the raccoon. It ate the fish it had lifted out. Then it grabbed another one. When the raccoon had eaten all the bait, it trotted up the sandy bank and into the woods.

"What a strange animal!" Jim thought. "That raccoon isn't afraid of anything when he finds a free dinner. This must be the second time he's come to camp. I saw raccoon tracks in the sand last night.

"I'd better tie down the cover of my bait pail. This was too handy for him. From now on, there'll be no more free dinners for hungry raccoons to grab!"

Cry Wolf!

For a few days, Carlos had been visiting at the Banks farm. Now it was his last day, and the family was at breakfast. As soon as Jack and Carlos had eaten, they decided to take a walk in the woods.

"Mr. Banks," Carlos said, "Jack told me there were bears in your woods. Do you think we'll see any this morning?"

Mr. Banks stood up and laughed. "There are no bears in our woods," he said. "Jack was just pretending. I'm afraid my son Jack pretends more than he should. Why, he once saw an elephant in the barnyard, a bear in the woods, and a monkey in an oak tree all in one morning!"

Jack's face started getting red.

"Son," Mr. Banks said, "that is the wrong kind of pretending. To 'cry wolf' like that may bring you trouble."

"Cry wolf?" Jack asked.

"Let me tell you a story," Mr. Banks said. "Long ago there was a boy who was supposed to watch over his father's sheep. He had to stay out on the hills all by himself, and he kept wishing something exciting would happen. One day, feeling things were too quiet, he called, 'Wolf! Wolf!' All the neighbors came running.

"The boy liked this new game. So the next day he cried, 'Wolf! Wolf!' again. Once more the neighbors came.

"The third day a wolf really did come. The boy yelled, 'Wolf! Wolf!' But not one of the neighbors came. They thought the boy was still playing his game."

"Do you think there might be a wolf in our woods?" Jack asked.

"Oh, Jack," said Mr. Banks as the boys went out, "you've missed the point!"

"I think I see a bear over there," Jack cried as he and Carlos raced across the cornfield. Carlos laughed and pointed to animals that he pretended to see.

Finally Carlos said, "I have to rest."

"All right," said Jack. "While you rest, I'll go look for a bear."

"You might even see a wolf," Carlos laughed. "Or better yet, an elephant!"

Jack ran to the lake. Suddenly he saw a deer standing in the path in front of him. The deer lifted its head and looked as if it were trying to smell something.

Then a second deer stepped from the woods and took a drink from the water.

Jack thought he had never seen anything so beautiful as those two deer. Perhaps there was a third one, too. He moved closer. The deer turned, saw him, and ran. The last he saw of them was their stand-up tails, looking like white flags.

Quickly Jack ran to where Carlos was. "I saw some deer!" he cried excitedly.

"How interesting!" Carlos said. "I saw some elephants. They were huge."

"But I really did see some deer!" Jack cried. "Don't you believe me?"

"Jack, if you really saw some deer, then I really saw some elephants," Carlos laughed. "Come on. Let's go home."

"Dad, I saw a deer!" Jack cried when the tired boys stood in the barnyard.

"Surely you saw two of them, didn't you?" Mr. Banks replied.

"There **were** two!" Jack cried. "How did you know?"

"Two deer are better than one," Mr. Banks laughed. "Carlos, you must go and get cleaned up. Your mother will be here for you in a short time."

After Carlos had left them, Jack looked at his father. "I guess I 'cried wolf' too many times, didn't I?" he asked.

Mr. Banks looked down at his son.

"Please," Jack begged, "I want you to believe me. Tomorrow I'll look again. They'll have to come to the lake to drink."

For a minute no one said anything.

Then Mr. Banks smiled at Jack. "If we get to the lake about sun-up," he said, "we may find them. I haven't seen deer in the woods since I was a boy."

A Zoo Baby

Through the glass of a large window, Susan Gray and her uncle could see the very newest animal in the city zoo. It was a baby elephant.

As they stood watching, they saw his huge mother carefully place a front leg on each side of him. Then she slowly started to rock herself and her baby back and forth, back and forth.

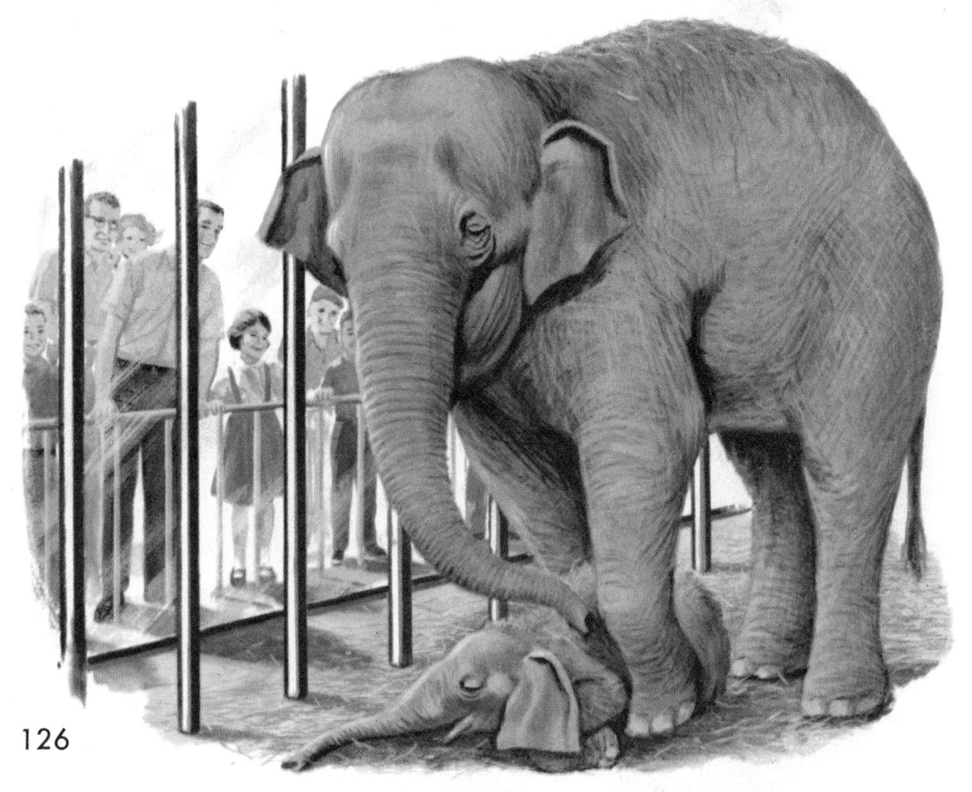

"Is that a game?" asked Susan.

"It could be a game," said her uncle. "But I think the mother elephant is just rocking her baby to sleep."

The huge elephant kept on rocking until a zoo keeper came along. He had some apples and a pail of water for the mother. She stopped rocking and reached out her trunk to the apples.

The baby elephant opened his eyes. He watched his mother eat an apple. Then he got up on his short legs and lifted his tiny trunk toward the apples.

But the little elephant couldn't use his trunk well enough yet to grab an apple. He tried and tried. All he could get into his mouth was the end of his trunk. So he just stood there until his mother had eaten all the apples.

As the zoo keeper was leaving, he saw Susan waving and pointing to something behind him. She seemed excited.

The man turned around quickly to see what was wrong. The little elephant was pushing his way through the bars!

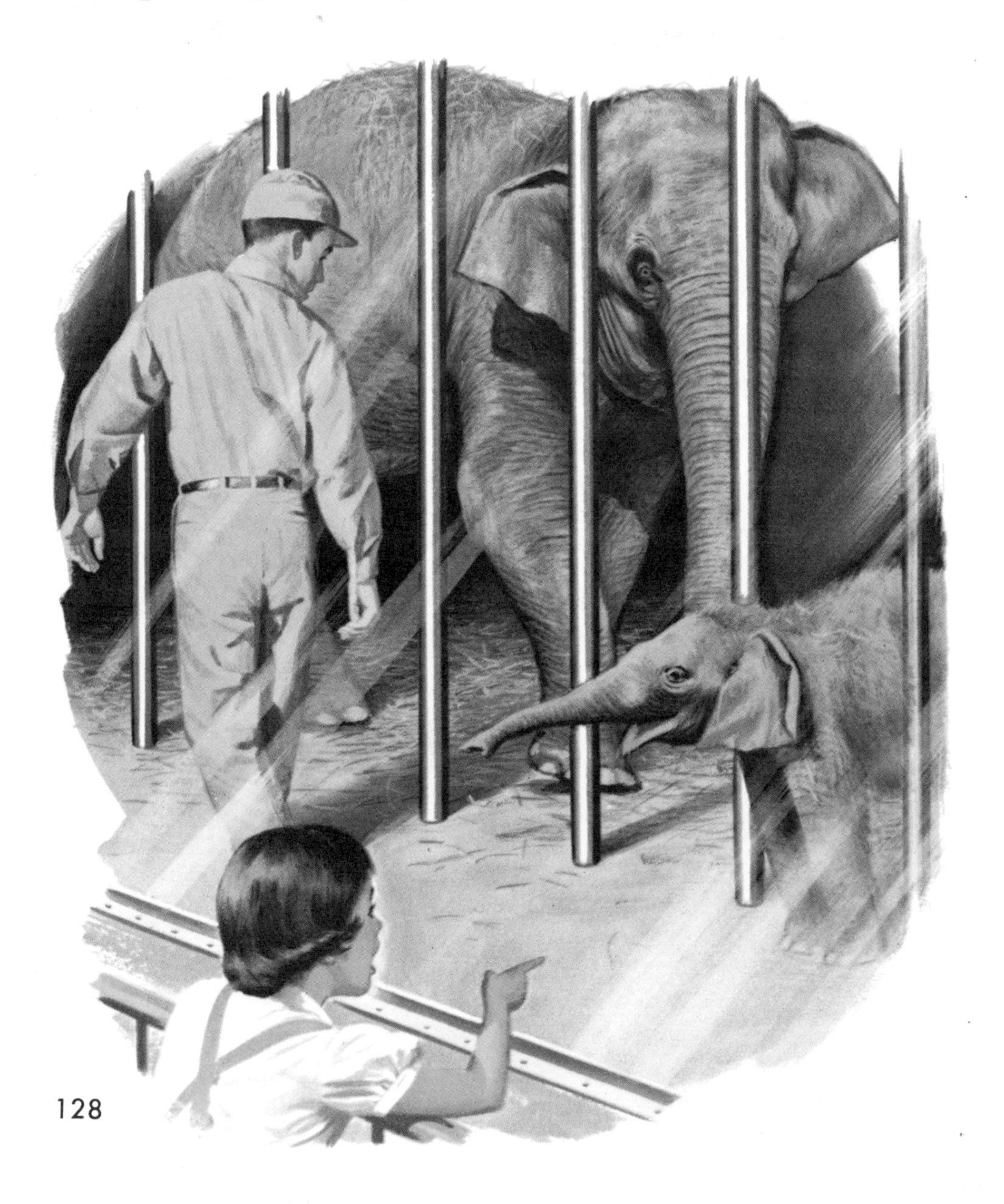

The zoo keeper gave a yell and ran to stop the baby. But the huge mother got to her son first. She reached her long trunk through the bars and grabbed him around the neck. Then with one pull she carefully brought him back behind the bars where he belonged.

The baby elephant did not want to be pulled back. He started to squeal, and everybody in the crowd laughed.

Suddenly the mother elephant walked over to the water pail. She filled her trunk with water. Then she turned and pointed her long trunk through the bars toward the window.

What a splash there was as the water hit the large window in front of Susan and her uncle!

"Well, I guess no mother wants people to laugh at her baby," said Susan to her uncle. "But who could help laughing at such a funny baby?"

A Wrong Guess

Early one morning Bill Banks went to feed his horse. He heard a call from the house just as he reached the barn.

"I'm going to town in ten minutes," Mr. Banks said. "I have to take care of a letter your mother wrote, and I have to get some oil. Do you want to come?"

"I surely do," replied Bill.

Bill turned to his sister Nancy, who was picking blueberries. "Will you feed Graylegs his breakfast?" Bill asked.

Nancy nodded to her older brother, and soon he and Mr. Banks rode off.

When Nancy had filled her pail with blueberries, she took them into the house and helped her mother clean them.

As they worked, Nancy's brother Jack came in. He watched until the blueberries were clean. Then he grabbed a few and put them in his mouth.

"Jack!" said Mrs. Banks. "You're not being very helpful. Nancy and I need these berries for cupcakes."

"Yes, we do," said Nancy. "But before we start baking, I must feed Graylegs. Bill went with Dad to get some oil."

"I'll feed him," offered Jack.

"Thanks," replied Nancy. "You'll get a cupcake before dinner for being so nice."

Nancy and her mother started to make the blueberry cupcakes. Soon a pan was ready for the oven. When it was baked, Mrs. Banks took the pan out of the oven. Then she left the kitchen to take care of some clothes that she was washing.

Since the cupcakes were too hot to be eaten, Nancy took them out of their pan. Then she put the eight hot cakes on the back porch, where a cool wind blew.

"I'll leave those hot cupcakes out there until they are cool," she thought as she shut the kitchen door. "Now I'll bake another pan of them."

A little later Nancy came out to see if the blueberry cupcakes on the porch were cool. Three of them were missing!

"I'm afraid I was wrong about Jack," she thought. "He's not such a nice boy after all. I told him he could have one cake before dinner. He has taken three!"

Nancy went back to the kitchen. By this time the second pan of cupcakes was baked. Nancy took it out of the oven.

All of a sudden the girl heard a bang. She put the hot pan on the kitchen table and ran to the porch. On the floor was the pan on which she had put the eight blueberry cupcakes to cool. Near it was one cupcake. The rest were gone!

Then she saw something strange. It was Graylegs with a cupcake in his mouth!

Nancy could not help laughing at the old horse. "Graylegs!" she said. "**You** ate those cakes that I left out here to cool. You're a bad, bad boy!"

Graylegs nodded his big gray head.

Just then Nancy heard Jack shouting in an excited way. "Graylegs is gone!" he yelled. "I didn't shut the door when I was getting his feed, and he trotted out of the barn. Now I can't find him."

"Come to the back porch," Nancy cried. "You'll see something strange here."

Jack ran up just as Graylegs grabbed the last cupcake from the porch floor.

"Well, well!" said Jack. "I thought I was supposed to feed you, Graylegs."

"You were," Nancy laughed. "But you don't need to feed him now. He has eaten eight cupcakes that I put out here to cool for our dinner today. It's too bad we can't eat the food that Graylegs was supposed to have eaten."

The Visiting Dog

Jimmy Day looked out the door of his new home. A strange dog was sitting on the front porch. It had black curly hair, long ears, and a happy-looking grin.

When Jimmy came out on the porch, the dog held up a paw for him to shake.

Jimmy shook the paw and said, "Hi!"

The dog gave an excited bark.

Jimmy offered the dog some cool water. "It's such a hot day I know you want a drink," he said. "Maybe you're hungry, too. I'll get you some food."

The dog started to drink the water at once. Soon the last drop was gone, and all the food was eaten. Then the dog held out its paw to shake hands again.

As Jimmy was shaking the paw, Mrs. Day came out. Jimmy said, "This lost dog needed food and water. May I keep him, teach him tricks, and take care of him?"

Mrs. Day nodded. "Yes," she said, "you may take care of the dog and pretend he belongs to you until we find his owner."

Jimmy wished he knew the dog's name. He looked at its black curls. All of a sudden he said, "Here, Curly!"

The dog gave another excited bark.

Jimmy laughed. "I wonder if Curly is your real name," he said. "That isn't a bad name for you, my little friend."

Jimmy looked in the paper to see if a black, curly-haired dog had been lost. He found nothing about any lost dog.

At lunchtime Jimmy left his new friend outside while he went in to eat. When he came out, the dog had gone.

"Curly! Curly!" the boy shouted.

The dog did not come, but Jimmy rushed back and forth and kept on calling him.

Finally Pat Gray shouted from the next yard, "Who on earth is Curly? Why are you calling him? What's wrong?"

"I was calling a dog," Jimmy said as he trotted over to where Pat stood.

"Is he your dog?" asked Pat.

"Oh, I'm not his real owner," replied Jimmy. "But I'd like to be. I found him sitting on our porch this morning. He has black curly hair, long ears, and a happy-looking grin. Do you know him?"

The other boy nodded. "That must be Rags," he said. "I'd like to own him, too. But he belongs to old Mr. Brown in that big brick house down there.

"Rags is a funny dog. He doesn't live with Mr. Brown very much. He goes to one house and stays for a few days. Then he goes on to visit someone else."

Jimmy cried, "Why, I've never heard of such a dog!"

"No, I don't suppose you have," said Pat. "I can't remember another visiting dog. But Rags has been one ever since I've lived in this neighborhood."

"Is Rags his real name?" Jimmy asked. "He barked when I called him Curly."

"Oh, he answers to almost any name," said Pat. "We all teach him tricks and take care of him. We give him food and all the water he wants to drink. He comes and goes as he pleases."

All of a sudden Jimmy heard a noise. There was the black dog rushing toward him with an old shoe in its mouth.

"Am I to wear that?" Jimmy asked.

"I forgot to tell you about that old shoe," Pat laughed. "Rags brings it with him when he comes to visit. When he lets the shoe fall, you're supposed to throw it. Then he runs and gets it.

"Rags brings the shoe only if he likes you. Since you came to our neighborhood only a short time ago, Rags wasn't sure if you would take good care of him. Now he's come with his shoe for you to throw. That shows he likes you."

"Well, I'm glad he does," said Jimmy. "And even if Rags doesn't stay long, we'll have fun while he's here."

The Hit of the Show

Mary Ann turned on the TV in time to hear a jolly man say, "Hello, hello! This is Uncle Jerry at River Park Zoo.

"Thank you for all the fine letters that you wrote me last week telling what you like best on this show. Keep on writing. I love to get such nice letters."

Uncle Jerry slowly began to walk down a sandy path that led past a pond.

"It certainly is a beautiful day here at River Park Zoo," he said in his jolly way. "I'd like to have every one of you here right now. But since most of you can't be at the zoo, I'm glad you're watching the show and hearing my words on TV."

Uncle Jerry kept right on talking as he came to a gate under some big oaks. "I have a wonderful surprise for you," he said. "This is the opening day of the new children's zoo at River Park.

"Many of the animals that you see in a big people's zoo may seem big and scary to you. But in this children's zoo the animals are very friendly. They almost seem to be asking to be petted.

"You'll soon be meeting some of these animals. When you do, you'll see just how friendly the animals are in this new part of the River Park Zoo."

Just then Uncle Jerry came to a hen with red feathers. "I'd like you to meet Mrs. Squawk," he said as he reached out to pat the hen's feathers. "She isn't the real mother of these six chickens, but she takes good care of them."

The red hen puffed up her feathers and squawked. Then she ran to catch up with the six chickens, who were ahead of her.

"Well," said Uncle Jerry. "Most of the time Mrs. Squawk is very friendly. All of a sudden she doesn't seem to like me."

Uncle Jerry went on down a path that led to some animals in pens. First he came to a raccoon that was eating its dinner. When it saw Uncle Jerry, it leaped to the front of its pen and held out a paw. In the paw was a fish.

"Thank you, Black Eyes," said Uncle Jerry in his jolly way. "But save that fish for yourself. I don't want one."

Uncle Jerry went on. Just ahead of him was a sheep in a pen. It seemed to be nodding to him. Then the sheep came over for the man to pet it.

In the third pen, two baby goats were drinking water. "Ba-a-a!" they called.

Uncle Jerry patted them, too.

All of a sudden a little monkey raced down from an oak tree and onto the path.

"Hi, there, Miss Monkey," said the man. "Let's see how friendly you are."

Uncle Jerry held out his left arm, and the monkey leaped onto it.

With loud squeals, the monkey climbed higher on Uncle Jerry's arm. She put one paw around his neck and patted the front of his shirt with the other.

Uncle Jerry cried, "Come now, Miss Monkey. That's enough! Get down!"

But Miss Monkey stayed where she was. With a happy grin, she pushed off Uncle Jerry's hat and pulled at his hair. Then she grabbed his handkerchief from his shirt pocket and covered his face.

Suddenly a zoo keeper saw what was happening and took the squealing monkey down. As he carried her away in his arms, the TV show came to an end.

Mary Ann told her grandmother about the show. Then she said, "I think I'll write a letter to Uncle Jerry. He was right. We did meet friendly animals at the children's zoo. Maybe he thought Miss Monkey was too friendly. But I thought she was the hit of the show!"

Firehouse Cat

Snowball was a big white cat that lived in a firehouse. Two years ago Snowball had been a tiny lost kitten. Fireman Pat had been looking for a lost glove and had found the kitten. He had brought it to the firehouse and named it Snowball. The cat had lived there ever since.

Snowball liked to sleep in front of the firehouse in the bright summer sun. But when the firebell rang, he would leap out of the way. He had to do this to keep from being stepped on or hit by the fire trucks as they left the brick building.

One day Snowball was sleeping there with his chin on his front paws. All at once the sun seemed very hot to Snowball. So he went inside and climbed onto the huge ladder truck. Slowly he curled up by a ladder and went to sleep.

All of a sudden the firebell rang!

Before the big cat could leap off the truck, firemen rushed to get on it. The truck's engine roared, and Snowball was on his way to a fire.

The huge ladder truck soon came to a squealing stop in front of a burning store. The hose truck pulled up just ahead of it. Firemen hopped off the trucks that they rode and began pulling at the hoses.

A large crowd of people was standing nearby, watching the bright fire. But the crowd moved back as Fireman Pat pulled the first hose toward the burning store.

In a few minutes water came rushing out of the hoses. It hit the fire with a loud roar.

The bright fire and the loud roaring noise scared Snowball. He curled up under the long ladders on the truck and tried his best to hide.

Just then firemen came running to put up the ladders. Snowball was pushed and bumped as the ladders above him were put into place.

The noises got louder and louder, and Snowball got more and more scared.

Firemen were shouting!

Engines were roaring!

Water was rushing from many hoses against the front of the burning store!

The cat was too scared to stay on the fire truck any longer. All of a sudden he leaped off and ran.

Finally the fire was out, and the people had left. The firemen were rolling up the hoses and setting the ladders back in the trucks.

As Fireman Pat went around to the side of the store, he heard a loud cry. He looked above his head and saw Snowball on a ladder.

"Snowball!" he cried. "I never knew you were here. Where did you come from?

"Don't fall, Snowball. I'll bring you down."

Fireman Pat began to climb the ladder that had been set against the brick wall.

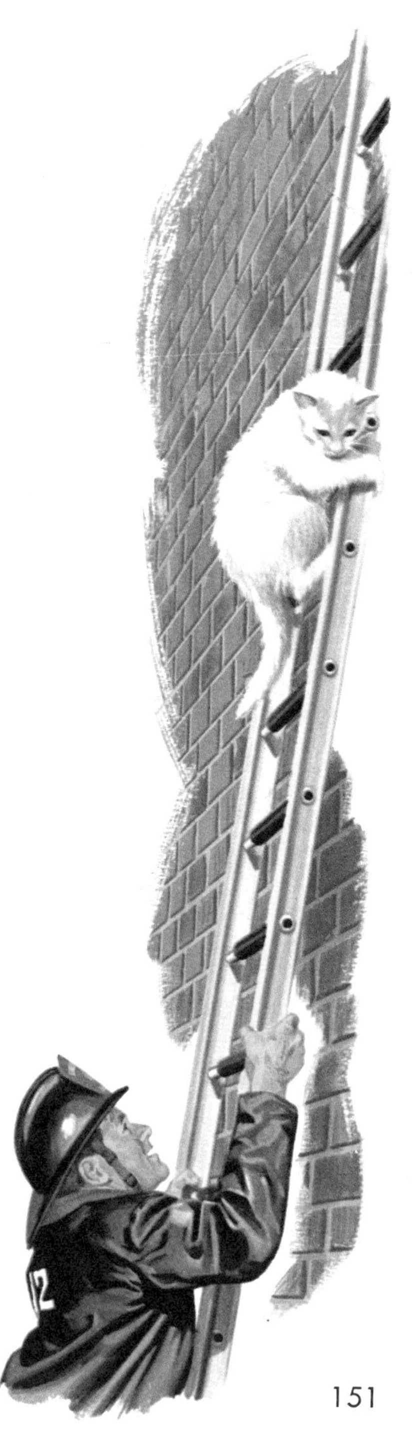

Soon the big white cat felt Pat's hands around him. He let go of the ladder and curled up against Pat's coat.

"That's right, Snowball," said Pat with a pleased grin. "Hang on to me."

Pat backed carefully down the ladder.

The other firemen had seen what was happening. They came to meet Pat and grinned as they patted Snowball. Then they got into the trucks, started the engines, and headed back to the firehouse.

When they reached the brick firehouse, Fireman Pat lifted the cat off the ladder truck. "Remember now, Snowball," he said. "No more fires for you!"

Snowball did not seem to be listening. He ran into the firehouse ahead of the men and started to wash himself.

But the men decided that he had heard every word Fireman Pat had said to him. Never again did Snowball leap onto a fire truck and go to sleep there.

Sonny

As she sat reading, Katy Burns could hear her bird whistling and hopping about inside its cage. Now and then as it sang, it said some words that it knew.

"Pretty bird!" Sonny sang. "Merry Christmas! Happy birthday! Whee!"

"Oh, Sonny," Katy laughed. "How on earth do you learn those funny things?"

Just then Mrs. Burns called. "Katy," she said, "Judy Ann has left the yard. I'm trying to find my gardening gloves. Will you please go and get your sister?"

Katy walked into the kitchen, where her mother was looking into things as she tried to find the missing gloves.

"I never saw such a girl for wanting to go away!" said Mrs. Burns.

For the third time that day, Katy went out looking for Judy Ann. "She likes to hide," Katy thought. "She does it as a game. She never goes very far."

Soon she saw Judy Ann at the corner of Third Street and Oak. An older girl was asking Judy Ann questions.

"Hi," Katy said. "That is my little sister. We have trouble keeping her at home. Mother says we need a big cage. Looking for her wears me out."

The older girl laughed. "Teach her your telephone number," she said. "That might take care of your troubles."

As the girls got home, Mrs. Burns found her gloves and went to the garden. Katy took Judy Ann to the living room.

"This is our telephone number," Katy said. "You are going to learn it. First listen to me. Then try to say it after me. 521-5448—521-5448—521-5448." She spoke very slowly.

Judy Ann worked hard for a while, but it was not easy to learn the number. Then she said that she felt tired.

"We'll try again tomorrow," said Katy. "Perhaps you can learn better then."

The next morning the girls worked on the number again. Sonny had been taken out of his cage, and he was flying about in the living room. Sometimes he sang his own funny songs. He sang in such a loud voice that Katy spoke to him and told him to be quiet.

Then Katy spoke to Judy Ann. "Maybe the number would be easier to learn if I made it into a song," she said. She began, "521-5448—521-5448—521—— "

"I'm tired of learning," Judy Ann said. "I want to play with Sonny."

But Sonny did not want to play. He flew into the kitchen. Just then Mrs. Burns came in from the garden. Out Sonny flew! Out the open door! Out past the garden and above the neighbor's garage!

"Oh, Mother!" Katy cried. "He just flew over Mr. Young's garage. Do you think I'll ever find him?"

"You follow him!" Mrs. Burns called. "I'll get his cage. Maybe if he sees it, he will want to get into it."

Katy and her mother went all around the neighborhood. They listened for the bird's songs. They called and called.

Finally they were walking along Third Street, feeling very sad. "Is there any chance he'll come home?" Katy asked.

Suddenly Mrs. Burns cried, "We left Judy Ann alone. We must hurry home!"

When they got there, Judy Ann was gone.

"I'll hang this cage on its hook," Katy said. "Then I'll go find her."

Just then the telephone on the kitchen wall rang. Mrs. Burns said, "Hello."

The voice on the other end of the line said, "This is Bob Wills. I found a little friend who told me this number."

"Bob," Mrs. Burns said, "this is Katy's mother. You've called our number."

"Oh," Bob laughed. "I'll bring my little friend over right away."

"Bob Wills has Judy Ann," Mrs. Burns said happily. "He's bringing her here."

In a few minutes the doorbell rang. Mrs. Burns and Katy rushed to the door.

"Where's Judy Ann?" Mrs. Burns cried.

"I don't know," Bob said. "But see my new little friend." He pointed to Sonny, who was sitting happily on the bill of Bob's baseball cap.

"That's a handy place to carry a bird," Bob went on. "And it was handy for me that he knew your telephone number."

"521-5448. Whee!" squawked Sonny.

Katy held out her hand, and Sonny hopped onto it. "Back to your cage," she said happily. "You flew too far today."

Just then Judy Ann came up the steps. "Katy," she said, "you forgot to come and look for me. I waited and waited at Mr. Young's garage, but you forgot to come!"

A Joke on Sandy

When George Willing came to work for Mr. Banks at Hill Farm, he did not come alone. He brought a puppy that belonged to him. The puppy's name was Sandy.

Dick Banks looked happily at the little dog. He hoped that he would get a chance to play with him. But Sandy stayed with George and followed him all day long.

One day George headed for the pigpen with corn for the pigs. Sandy was close behind. George told Sandy to stay out of the pen. But when he opened the gate, Sandy rushed in ahead of him.

What a sound of grunting there was! The pigs saw the puppy and came at him with a rush. Sandy barked and ran after the grunting pigs. Around and around the pigpen raced the barking dog and the grunting pigs.

Above all this barking and grunting came another sound. It was George yelling, "Sandy! Leave those pigs alone!"

Dick heard the sounds and rushed to the pigpen. Just as he got close enough to see what was happening, he heard the puppy give a strange little bark. Then he saw Sandy run over to George. The dog ran on three legs. He did not use his left front foot at all.

George picked the puppy up and held him against his shirt. Carefully he felt Sandy's left front paw.

At last George spoke. "Sandy's paw has been hurt," he said. "It got stepped on when the pigs chased him. The paw should be tied up. I saw an old shirt in the toolhouse. I can use part of it."

George carried Sandy to the toolhouse. Dick raced ahead to open the door.

Dick laughed when he saw the paw tied up in part of the shirt. Sandy looked as if he were wearing a white boot.

"That's all I can do," George told Dick. "The foot will soon get well."

Each day Dick stayed beside Sandy, keeping him quiet. He petted Sandy and talked to him. He brought him food to eat and water to drink. At night he made him a good bed in the garage.

Dick went on taking care of the puppy. After eight days Sandy felt much better.

One bright morning when Dick went to the garage, Sandy chased him out into the barnyard and ran happily about. But he did not try to use his left foot.

When George came in from the fields that day, he picked Sandy up and looked at his paw. "This foot ought to be fine now," he told Dick. "We won't keep it tied up any more."

Soon George put the dog down. At once Sandy ran off, chasing Dick's kitten onto a pile of bricks near the garage.

"Look, George!" Dick cried. "Sandy isn't using his left front foot as he ought. Do you think it is well yet?"

"Oh, yes," said George. "Sandy will soon be walking on all four feet."

For the rest of the day, Dick kept his eyes on Sandy. But he didn't see the dog use his left front foot at all.

Near bedtime Dick told George that Sandy was still walking on three legs.

George just laughed. "I can get Sandy to use that left front foot," he told Dick. "I'll trick that pup. Just wait until tomorrow. I'll play a joke on him then."

The next day George tied up the dog's right front foot, and Sandy ran off.

Dick cried, "Look, George! Sandy isn't using his other front foot now!"

"No," laughed George. "Sandy thinks he ought not to run on that foot because it's tied up. We'll leave it tied up just long enough for Sandy to learn that his left foot is well."

In a short time the puppy was running on all four feet. George's joke on Sandy had worked very well!

The Baby Fox

Mr. Banks and his two youngest sons had left their car to take a walk in the woods. Beside a big tree they found a baby fox alone. His eyes were shut.

"Why is he so quiet?" whispered Dick. "Is something wrong?"

"He needs food," Mr. Banks whispered back. "Something must have happened to his mother. This baby fox won't have a chance to live if he's left alone.

"We'll take him home with us. You and Jack can look after him until he gets stronger."

Mr. Banks took the baby fox in his arms and carried him to the car. Then the man and his sons rode home.

Before long the car came to a stop at the family garage. The boys hopped out and hurried to find a box. They put an old shirt in it to make a bed, and Mr. Banks carried the fox over to it.

The boys placed a little pile of food and a pan of cool water near the fox's chin. Then they sat and watched him.

The fox opened his eyes, but he did not make a sound. He did not act interested in the food that had been set beside him.

At last Jack whispered, "Maybe we ought to leave him alone. Then he may eat. I'm sure he'll grow stronger after he has eaten some food."

The boys left the garage, but the next morning they were back early. Most of the food and water was gone. The baby fox could even take a few steps.

The fox kept on growing stronger. Soon he was acting like a pet. The boys named him Foxy and played with him as if he were a puppy. He even learned a trick.

One morning at breakfast, Mr. Banks said, "Foxy is growing up fast. So far he's stayed in the yard. But soon he may jump the fence and go over to our neighbor's farm. Then he might chase the chickens. He ought to be tied up."

The boys' father tied Foxy to the back porch, but one day the fox got away. The boys found him chasing their neighbor's hens. The hens were squawking, and the neighbor was yelling.

The neighbor scared off the fox, and the boys took their pet home. Then they told Mr. Banks what Foxy had done.

The boys' father shook his head. "I was afraid this might happen," he said. "Your pet is a wild animal. Now that he's growing up and getting stronger, he's starting to act like one.

"A wild animal is not happy when he's kept behind bars or tied up. Foxy is strong enough now to care for himself. We must give him a chance to be free."

The boys felt very sad, but they knew that their father was right. They gave Foxy a big breakfast and watched him eat it. Then they put their pet in the car and rode off with their father.

When they reached the big oak where they had found him, Mr. Banks stopped the car. Jack opened the car door and set the fox free.

"Good-by, Foxy!" cried both boys.

The fox leaped toward some bushes beside the road. For a few minutes he ran back and forth. Then he turned and came back toward the car.

"How strange Foxy acts," Jack said. "I don't think he wants to be free."

All of a sudden the animal stopped and lifted his head. He looked as if he might be listening to faraway sounds.

As the three watched, the fox ran up a hill and into some bigger bushes. This time Foxy did not come back. He had gone to live with the wild foxes. Soon he would be as wild as they were.

STORYBOOK FRIENDS

The Hare and the Hedgehog

One bright, sunny morning a hedgehog was sitting at the door of his home.

Suddenly he decided that a walk before breakfast might be good for him. So off he went. He had not gone far when he saw a hare under a berry bush.

"Good morning, Neighbor Hare," the friendly hedgehog called.

The hare seemed very much surprised to see his neighbor. "Why are you out so early?" he asked.

"I want to find out how my turnips are growing," answered the hedgehog. "I'm taking a walk to the turnip field."

The hare gave a loud laugh. "Taking a walk!" he said. "It must be very hard to walk on legs as short as yours."

That made the hedgehog very angry. "I suppose you think long legs are much better than short ones," he said. "Well, let's find out. Let's run a race in the turnip field to see if they are."

"Very well," said the hare with a grin. "No sooner said than done."

And the hare started off to the field.

"Wait!" called the hedgehog. "I want to eat breakfast first. I'll meet you at the turnip field in a few minutes."

Then away went the hedgehog as fast as his short legs could carry him.

When the hedgehog reached home, he asked his wife to go to the turnip field with him. On the way he told her about the race.

Then he said, "You can easily help me play a joke on the hare. He will run up the first row of turnips. I will start up the second row. You can hide at the top of my row and wait. When the hare gets to the top of his row, you must jump out and say, 'I'm here first.'"

Soon the hedgehog and his wife came to the turnip field. He went at once to the bottom of the second row. His wife ran to hide at the top of the same row.

The hedgehog waited until the hare got to the bottom of the first row. Then he spoke. "Let's start," he cried.

"Fine," said the hare. "Ready! Go!" And away he ran with all his might.

But the hedgehog took only two steps. Then he stopped still and waited under the cool turnip leaves.

Just before the hare got to the top of his row, a hedgehog popped out. "I'm here first!" said the hedgehog.

"Well, well!" said the surprised hare. "This is very strange. Let's race back to the bottom of our rows."

He turned and dashed down his row as fast as the wind. But before he reached the bottom of the row, he saw a hedgehog pop out.

"I'm here first!" said the hedgehog.

This time the hare was very angry. "We must race again!" he shouted.

The hedgehog laughed to himself over the joke he and his wife were playing. "No sooner said than done!" he cried. "Ready! Go!"

The hare went leaping up his row. But just before he reached the top, the hedgehog's wife popped up her head.

She called out, "I'm here first again! You act very tired, Neighbor Hare."

The angry hare did not even stop to answer. He huffed and puffed and dashed to the bottom of the row.

Back and forth dashed the hare. Each time one hedgehog or the other popped out and said, "I'm here first!"

Finally the hare gave up. He had huffed and puffed so much that he couldn't race any more. Without saying a word, he hopped slowly off to his home in the bushes.

The hedgehogs stayed in the field and ate turnips until they were full. Both of them wondered if the angry hare would ever boast about his long legs again.

The Quarrel

Once an elephant and a monkey had a quarrel. Both animals were very proud. The huge elephant was proud because he was so strong. The little monkey was proud because he was so quick.

"I can pull down the biggest tree," boasted the elephant.

"Well, I could climb that tree before you could take even one step," boasted the monkey.

The elephant shouted, "It is better to be strong than to be quick!"

"No!" cried the angry monkey. "It is much better to be quick!"

The quarrel got louder and louder. At last a wise old owl questioned them. He asked what the quarrel was about.

Quickly the elephant spoke up. "Owl," he said, "tell us which is better. Is it better to be strong or to be quick?"

The owl thought for a minute before he answered the quarreling animals. Then the owl said, "Do as I tell you and you will learn which is better.

"Go to the river and swim across it. On the other side you'll find a tree with beautiful fruit growing on it. Pick some of the fruit and bring it to me."

The elephant and the monkey hurried to the river. Now this river was a very deep one. When the monkey saw it, he felt afraid. He did not want to take the chance of crossing it.

But the proud elephant said, "I am big, and I am stronger than you. Get on my back, and I'll take you across the river."

So the monkey climbed on the back of the elephant. Together they crossed the deep river.

A tall tree was growing on the bank of the river. Beautiful fruit was hanging from every branch. The elephant lifted his trunk to pick the fruit. But even the lowest branch was out of his reach.

Then the elephant tried to pull the tall tree down. He could not even shake it.

The monkey began to laugh. "You may be large and strong," he said. "But I see that you need some help. I'll dash up that tree and drop the fruit to you."

The little monkey easily climbed the tall tree. He picked some of the finest fruit and dropped it to the elephant.

It was not long before the elephant's mouth was too full to hold any more.

Quickly the monkey came sliding down the tall fruit tree. With one leap he was on the elephant's back. The two animals crossed the river again and went to the owl's home in the forest.

"We have brought you the finest of the fruit," the monkey called to the owl. "We have done what you told us to do. But we haven't learned if it is better to be strong or to be quick."

The owl said, "Just remember how you got the fruit. The elephant was strong enough to cross the deep river with you on his back. You were quick enough to climb the tall tree and pick the fruit.

"Being strong alone or quick alone was not enough. It took both of you to get the fruit from the tall tree."

The two animals slowly nodded their heads. Never again did the monkey or the elephant act so proud. Never again did they have that kind of quarrel.

A Boy and His Goats

Every morning a boy took his goats to a high, grassy hill. Every morning his three goats leaped and skipped to the top of the hill. There they ate good green grass until they were full.

Every evening the boy climbed the hill to drive his three goats home. But one evening the goats skipped over a fence into a cornfield. The boy followed them, but he could not get them out of the field. There they were, and there they stayed.

The boy did not know what to do. He sat down and began to cry.

As the boy sat crying in the cornfield, a hare came dashing up to the fence.

"Why are you crying?" asked the hare.

The boy replied, "I'm crying because I can't get my goats out of this field."

"I'll get them out," boasted the hare.

He leaped over the bars of the fence and started to chase the goats. But he could not get them out.

At last the hare sat down beside the boy. He, also, began to cry.

Then along came a fox who asked the hare why he was crying.

"I'm crying because the boy is crying," the hare said in answer to the question. "The boy cries because he can't make his three goats come out of the cornfield."

"I'll get them out," boasted the fox.

He jumped over the fence and chased the goats. But they would not get out.

So the fox sat down beside the hare. He, also, began to cry.

Soon a great big wolf came out of the forest and asked the fox why he was crying.

The fox said, "I'm crying because the hare is crying. The hare cries because the boy cries. The boy cries because he can't get his goats out of the field."

"I'll get them out," boasted the wolf.

He jumped over the fence and started chasing the goats. But they would not leave the cornfield.

So the great big wolf sat down beside the fox. He, also, began to cry.

After a while a bee flew near. "Why are you crying?" it asked the wolf as it buzzed by.

"I'm crying because the fox is crying," said the wolf. "The fox cries because the hare cries. The hare cries because the boy cries. And the boy cries because he can't get his three goats out of the cornfield. He has been crying the most."

The bee said, "It's foolish to cry. I can get the goats out very easily."

At the bee's words the wolf, the fox, the hare, and the boy stopped crying and began to laugh.

Finally the wolf said, "How can a tiny bee do what a great big wolf can't do?"

"Buzz! Buzz!" said the bee. "That's easy. The goats won't like my sting."

Away buzzed the bee. When it found the goats, it flew right to the biggest one and began stinging its ear.

The bee's sting hurt the biggest goat very much. He began to skip and kick and run. The two other goats saw what the bee had done. They, also, started to skip and kick and run.

All three goats wanted to get far, far away from the stinging bee. Soon they had jumped over the fence and were on their way home.

Johnny Cake

An old woman, an old man, and a boy lived together in an old, old house.

One day the woman took some eggs and other things and made a round cake for the evening dinner. She put the cake into a pot that stood beside the chimney. Then she put the pot on the chimney fire.

"Don't let my round Johnny Cake burn," she told the boy.

The old woman and the old man went to get wood in the nearby forest.

The boy sat by the chimney to watch the big round cake.

Soon the boy saw the pot cover lift a little. He thought that the pot was too full, so he took the cover off and set it against the chimney.

Out popped Johnny Cake! He rolled away from the chimney and across the floor. Then he rolled out the door.

The boy skipped after him. "Stop!" he cried. "Stop, Johnny Cake!"

The old woman and the old man heard the boy calling. They left the forest and they, too, ran after Johnny Cake.

But not one of them ran fast enough to catch the big, round, yellow cake.

On down the middle of the road rolled Johnny Cake. He felt happy as he rolled along, and he started to sing.

"This game is great fun!
I roll and they run."

Soon Johnny Cake rolled past a bear. "Where are you going?" called the bear.

"On and on," Johnny Cake called back. "I've rolled away from a boy, a woman, and a man.

"I can roll away from you, too."

The bear roared, "I'll see about that!"

Away the bear ran down the middle of the road. But he was too fat and slow to catch Johnny Cake.

As Johnny Cake went singing along, he crossed a big field full of farm workers. He called out, "I've rolled away from a boy, a woman, a man, and a bear.

"I can roll away from you, too."

The workers chased Johnny Cake, but not one of them could catch him.

Johnny Cake went rolling along and singing until he saw a sly fox. The fox was resting beside a pile of sticks.

Johnny Cake called out, "I've rolled away from a boy, a woman, a man, a bear, and a field full of workers.

"I can roll away from you, too."

The sly fox did not even move.

Johnny Cake rolled up closer, singing,

"This game is great fun.
I roll and they run."

The fox did not move or answer him.

So Johnny Cake went on, "I've rolled away from a boy, a woman, a man, a bear, and a field full of workers.

"I can roll away from you, too."

When the fox still did not answer him, foolish Johnny Cake rolled up to the sly fox's chin. For the third time he said, "I've rolled away from a boy, a woman, a man, a bear, and a field full of workers.

"I can roll away from you, too."

"Oh, you can, can you?" said the fox.

And as quick as could be, the sly fox grabbed Johnny Cake and ate him.

Brother Alonzo

The sun came up over the churchyard. All the animals were up, and all the brothers, too. Well, almost all!

Brother Alonzo was still sleeping. He was up late the night before with his friend, Clop-Clop. Old Clop-Clop, the horse, had a little cold, and Brother Alonzo had helped him get well.

Brother Alonzo was always helping someone. He was loved by Clop-Clop and all the other animals in the churchyard.

He was loved by all the animals in the forest.

He was loved by all the people in the town.

When Brother Alonzo did get up that morning, he said, "My, what a beautiful day!" Then he thought, "If there was only some way I could show my thanks to God."

He went into the church and thought and thought, "What gift can I give as thanks?"

Then he thought of the big, big church he had seen in the town. "Why, yes! I'll build a big church!"

So Brother Alonzo started to build a church. He put stones on top of each other—higher and higher and higher—until he could go no higher.

But all he had was a wall.

Brother Alonzo was very sad.

"There is more to building a big church than sticking stones on top of each other," he thought.

Then he heard a little sound. M-E-O-W! A kitten was caught in a tree.

"Please help me!" the kitten cried.

Brother Alonzo climbed on top of his stone wall so that he could reach the kitten and save her.

"Thank you," said the kitten "I'm glad you made a wall and could save me."

"So am I," answered Brother Alonzo. "But I was trying to build a big church."

"Why don't you paint a beautiful picture?" asked the kitten.

So Brother Alonzo got some paint in the town and went to a pretty spot on a hill. There he began painting. BUT HE JUST GOT PAINT ALL OVER!

On the way back to town, Brother Alonzo painted a bird cage and a toy clown for a little boy.

But still he was sad.

A pretty bird saw the brother and asked him, "Why are you so sad?"

"I have tried to give a gift to God, but I cannot," said Brother Alonzo.

"Why don't you write a song? That would be a wonderful gift to give God," said the bird.

All the animals came to hear Brother Alonzo's song. They soon hurried away.

Then along came another little boy. He was crying. "What is wrong?" asked Brother Alonzo.

"My little dog Yip-Yip is lost," cried the boy.

Brother Alonzo helped the boy look for Yip-Yip. They looked high and low, near and far.

"Maybe he could hear your song if you played it very loud," said the boy.

So the brother did just that, and Yip-Yip came running back.

Brother Alonzo still was not happy as he walked back to his room.

Mr. Wise Old Owl was waiting for him.

"I can't do anything to please God," the brother cried out loud. "I can't build a church, or paint a picture, or play a song!"

"Wait a minute!" shouted Mr. Wise Old Owl. "You have told me all that you could not do. Now let me tell you what you **could** and **did** do!"

"You used your church wall to save a kitten. Your painting made a little boy glad. And Yip-Yip was found by your song.

"You have been good and kind. That is the best gift in all the world!" said Mr. Wise Old Owl.

Suddenly Brother Alonzo smiled—happily. And I am sure God smiled, too.

A Foolish Rabbit

Once there was a foolish little rabbit who was afraid most of the time. One day she was resting under a tall tree in the middle of the forest. Suddenly something fell and landed on the ground near her.

"What made that queer noise?" she said to herself. Then something hit her on the head. She looked up, but all she saw was the blue sky.

The foolish little rabbit did not see the thing that fell. But she heard the queer sound that it made when it landed.

"The sky is surely falling in!" cried the rabbit as she went leaping through the forest.

Soon the foolish rabbit met a second rabbit. "Run! Run!" begged the foolish little rabbit.

"Run for your life!
Run for your life!
The sky is falling in!"

The second rabbit started to run also. "Run!" he cried in a scared voice.

"Run for your life!
Run for your life!
The sky is falling in!"

Soon all the rabbits in the forest began running and shouting. They cried,

"Run for your life!
Run for your life!
The sky is falling in!"

A bird heard the rabbits' words. It stopped singing and flew off, calling,

"Run for your life!
The sky is falling in!"

A fox down below was the first to hear the bird.

The fox told a wildcat.

The wildcat told a wolf.

The wolf told a bear.

They all galloped off through the forest. As they ran, they shouted,

"Run for your life!
The sky is falling in!"

The animals kept on calling and running until old King Lion suddenly barred the path.

"Stop right there!" roared the lion. "I want to ask you a question. Which one of you saw the sky fall in?"

"Not I, King Lion," replied the bear. "The wolf told me about it."

"Not I!" replied the wolf. "A wildcat told me."

"Not I!" replied the wildcat. "A fox told me."

"Not I!" replied the fox. "A little bird told me."

Finally one scared rabbit pointed to the foolish little rabbit and said, "She is the one who told us!"

King Lion spoke to the foolish rabbit. "Why did you think the sky was falling in?" he asked her.

"I heard it, King Lion," answered the little rabbit. "I heard it myself."

"How queer!" said the lion. "I heard no strange noise ringing through the woods. Show me where you heard the sound."

Off they both went to the middle of the deep forest.

The rabbit led the lion to the tall tree under which she had been resting. Just then a big nut fell to the ground.

"You silly bunny!" cried King Lion. "It was only a nut that you heard fall!"

"Oh!" said the foolish rabbit. "Then the sky is not falling in after all."

"No!" roared King Lion in an angry voice. "Go and tell the other animals that you were wrong."

"I shall do what you say, King Lion," said the foolish little rabbit.

Off she raced through the deep forest, shouting,

"The sky is not falling in!
I was wrong! I was wrong!
I only heard a nut fall."

"So that's all it was," said the bear.

Then he and the other animals galloped back to their homes, calling as they ran,

"The sky is not falling in!
The sky is not falling in!"

Why the Bear Has a Short Tail

One winter afternoon a bear met a fox with a line of fish hung on his back.

"What fine fish!" said the bear. "I'd surely like a chance to catch some fish like those for myself. How did you catch them on a winter day?"

Now the fox was as sly as sly can be. He didn't want the bear to know that he really hadn't caught the fish himself. So he just said, "Catching fish in winter is easy. These are for my supper."

The bear looked sad. He said that he hadn't eaten fish since winter had come.

The fox laughed to himself. "Well," he said, "go to the pond and cut a hole in the ice. Put your long, bushy tail in the hole. Then wait for the fish to bite.

"When the fish bite your tail, it may sting and hurt a little. But you must sit there as long as you can.

"The longer you sit with your tail in the pond, the more fish you will catch. When you think you have enough, pull out your tail with a quick, strong pull. A tail like yours is very handy.

"Now remember all I've told you."

"Thank you," said the bear with a nod. "That seems a queer way to catch fish, but I shall certainly try it for myself. I hope the fish will bite."

The sly, grinning fox watched the bear hurry off to the pond. Then he rushed home to eat a good fish supper.

At the pond the bear cut a hole in the ice wide enough for his bushy tail. He sat down and hung his tail in the water below. Then he waited for the fish to start biting.

The water seemed to grow colder and colder. The bear's tail grew colder, too. It began to sting and hurt. But the bear only grunted and grunted. He believed that his tail was stinging and hurting because the fish were biting it.

At sundown the bear finally decided he had enough fish for his supper. He tried to get up and pull out the fish he thought he had caught.

The poor bear huffed and puffed, but he could not stand up. While he had been sitting there, the water had turned to ice. The part of the bear's tail that hung in the pond was caught fast.

At first the bear was very angry. Then he remembered what the fox had told him. He gave a quick pull and a strong pull, too. Out of the ice came his tail!

But only part of it came out—and the shorter part at that! The longer, bushy part stayed fast in the ice.

All this happened long ago. Since that winter day all the bears on earth have very short tails.

And even to this day all the foxes on earth like to play jokes and are as sly as sly can be.

The Turtle Who Talked Too Much

Many, many years ago a young turtle lived on the sands by a quiet lake. He grew tired of living there and seeing the same turtles day after day.

"It would be nice to visit new places as birds do," he said. "But I can't fly. I can only crawl along on the ground. I'm just a poor turtle who can't go far."

From morning until night he could be heard talking in his squeaky voice.

Finally a wise old turtle spoke up and said, "One day you will surely wish you had not talked so much."

Summer turned into fall, and the days grew cooler. One day the old turtle said, "It is almost time to crawl into the sand and sleep all winter."

The young turtle didn't want to do this. He never stopped talking about going to a new, warmer land.

Two wild geese were swimming in the lake. They saw the young turtle crawling on the sand and heard his squeaky voice as he spoke of going to warm places.

"Come with us," said the geese. "We are leaving today for a warmer part of the country. We are going where days are always bright and sunny."

"How will I get there?" squeaked the turtle. "I can't go there by myself."

"We shall carry you," said the geese. "But you must keep your mouth shut."

"I can do that easily," said the turtle.

Then he heard a queer laugh as the old turtle crawled slowly past him.

The two wild geese walked across the sand and returned with a long stick.

"Catch hold of this with your mouth," they told the young turtle.

The turtle opened his wide mouth and caught hold of the middle of the stick.

"Bite it hard," cried the geese.

Then each one took an end of the stick in his mouth and lifted his wings.

Up went the big gray birds. As they flew across the lake, the turtle hung on with all his might. How fine it was to be carried to a warmer land by the strong wings of the geese!

Soon the geese were winging their way over a tiny pond. Down below some boys were fishing.

One boy cried, "See those wild geese carrying a turtle. What a silly turtle! It thinks it can fly!"

The boy's joking words made the turtle very angry. He started to say, "Why do you care what I am doing?"

But he only gave a squeaky sound. For when he opened his mouth to talk, he let go of the stick. Straight into the pond dropped the turtle. And there he stayed for the rest of his life!

The Man Who Kept House

Once there was a farmer who believed his work was too hard. He thought it was terrible. Each evening when he returned from his fields, he would ask his wife what she did all day.

"I kept house," she always answered.

The farmer would say, "Oh, your work is easy. I wish I had nothing to do but churn the butter, bring in the eggs, get supper, and watch the baby."

One evening the man's wife grew tired of hearing about her easy work. So she said, "Tomorrow I'll work in the fields, and you shall keep house."

"Fine!" said the man. "Keeping house will be no trouble at all for me."

The next morning the wife went straight to the fields, while the farmer started to do the housework. First he filled the churn with cream to make butter.

Suddenly he remembered that he hadn't seen the baby since his wife had gone. "Something terrible may have happened to our baby," thought the poor man.

But the baby was only playing in the flower garden. The man caught her up in his arms and returned to the house.

Beside the churn stood a pig! It had knocked over the churn and was drinking the cream that ran out.

"This is terrible!" said the man as he picked up the churn.

Stamping his foot, the farmer roared at the squealing pig. He chased it outside and put more cream in the churn.

Suddenly he remembered that he had not yet taken water to the cow. "This is terrible!" he said, huffing and puffing.

The man put the baby to bed and went off to draw water from the well. But he came back to get the churn. He couldn't take a chance on leaving it where the pig might knock it over again.

With the churn under one arm, the man stamped down the path to the well.

The farmer leaned over to get the rope that hung in the well. As he leaned over, the cream ran straight into the well below.

The angry farmer put down the churn and grabbed the rope. Then he began to draw up water for the cow. After his cow had had enough to drink, he started to take her to a grassy field.

Suddenly he remembered that the baby was sleeping in the house. "Oh, this is terrible!" cried the poor farmer. "Baby should not be left alone. But what shall I do with the cow?"

The man looked at the tall grass that grew on the roof of his house. How he wished his cow had wings! Then she could fly up there and eat grass.

All at once he thought of a way to get the cow up on the roof. "I will make a bridge for her," he said to himself.

First he led the animal to the top of a small hill behind the house. Then he got a long, wide board and placed it from the hilltop to the roof. After that he led the cow across the bridge onto the roof.

The man returned to the kitchen. He was getting more cream to churn when he suddenly remembered that he had not yet started to cook dinner. He filled a large pot with water and set it in the fireplace to warm.

Just then the poor man remembered the cow on the roof above. "Oh, this is terrible!" he cried. "The cow might fall and hurt herself."

Quickly he ran outside and got a long rope. He crossed the board to the roof and tied one end of the rope around the cow's horns. The other end of the rope he dropped down the chimney. Then the man came back into the house.

He ran to the chimney and caught hold of the rope. After drawing it down into the room, he tied it around his boot top.

"There!" he said, stamping his foot. "Now the cow can't fall off the roof and hurt herself. Now I can cook dinner."

At that minute the cow went sliding off the roof. As she fell, the rope began drawing the man up the chimney. There was the cow hanging outside the house by the rope on her horns. There was the poor man hanging upside down in the chimney by the rope on his foot. He was right above the pot of warm water.

The man could not help himself. He could not get up the chimney. He could not get down. He could only roar in a gruff voice.

The man's wife saw the cow hanging from the roof. She quickly cut the rope and let the poor cow down.

At that very second the wife heard a splash in the house. She ran in and saw the farmer with his legs up the chimney and his head in the cooking pot. All the water had splashed out over the floor.

The wife helped the man out of the pot. Then she cleaned the house, churned the butter, and cooked some food.

While his wife worked, the man leaned back in his chair. Never again did he offer to keep house.

Three Billy Goats Gruff

Long, long ago there were three goats named Gruff. All three liked to eat the grass on a nearby hill.

Now the shortest path to the hill was straight across a wooden bridge over a wide, deep river.

Under the bridge a mean and ugly troll was always hiding. The ugly troll had a great, loud voice that scared everybody who crossed the bridge.

One day Little Billy Goat Gruff started across the river.

Trip, trap! Trip, trap! Trip, trap! skipped his tiny feet on the bridge.

Suddenly there was a roar below him.

"Who is walking across my bridge?" called the troll.

"It is I," replied the goat in a scared, squeaky voice. "I'm going up the hill to eat grass and make myself fat."

"No! I'm going to gobble you up!" the ugly troll roared.

"Oh, please don't!" cried the little goat. "Wait! Wait for Big Billy Goat Gruff. He is much bigger than I."

"Be off with you, then," said the troll.

After a while the second goat started across the wooden bridge.

Trip, trap! Trip, trap! Trip, trap! went his feet on the boards.

The ugly troll leaned out and roared, "Who is walking across my bridge?"

"It is I," said the goat. "I'm going up the hill to eat grass and make myself fat."

"No!" shouted the ugly old troll. "I'm going to gobble you up."

The frightened goat begged, "Oh, wait! Wait for Great Big Billy Goat Gruff. He is much bigger than I."

"Be off with you, then," said the troll.

The mean old troll sat and waited. By and by he heard the third goat start over the wooden bridge.

TRAP! TRAP! TRAP! TRAP! stamped the large goat's feet.

"Who is stamping across my bridge?" called the troll in his loudest voice.

The third goat answered, "It is I. It is Great Big Billy Goat Gruff. I am going up the hill to eat grass and make myself grow fat."

Roaring like a lion, the troll jumped up on the bridge. "Oh, no! You'll not go to the hill today!" he cried. "I've been waiting for you ever since morning. I'm going to gobble you up!"

Great Big Billy Goat Gruff shook his great big horns at the ugly troll. "You don't frighten me a bit!" roared the goat. "Just try to gobble me up! Just try it! I'm going to knock you straight down into the river!"

The very next second the goat banged against the troll with his big horns.

Down into the wide river fell the troll. Straight down to the bottom he fell with a most terrible roar.

That was the end of the ugly troll!

After that the three goats grew so fat that they could hardly walk. As far as anyone knows, they are very fat yet.

City Mouse and Country Mouse

One summer day a city mouse went to visit a friend in the country.

The country mouse was very poor and lived all alone in a tiny house of straw. She had nothing but seeds and plants for food. So seeds and plants were what she gave her friend to eat.

The city mouse took one bite. "Oh," she said, "how silly you are to live in a straw house and eat this kind of food! Come with me to the city. You will have cakes and pies to eat there!"

The country mouse wanted to leave at once. But the city mouse thought they ought to wait until after dark to go. So that is what they did.

Late that night they got to the house where the city mouse lived. They ran under the house and crawled up through a hole in the floor. Then they were in a warm room full of wonderful smells.

On a table were ten cream puffs, a big pink cake, and a fruit pie.

The little country mouse could hardly believe what she saw. Her eyes opened wide. Wiggle, wiggle went her long tail as she tried to decide which good thing to bite into first.

At last she bit into a cream puff and gave an excited squeal. "Oh!" she said. "How clever you were, my friend, to find this house to live in! I don't think I'll ever return to my country home and eat just seeds and plants."

All of a sudden the city mouse saw two fierce, green-colored eyes close by.

"Run! Run!" she cried to the country mouse. "Be quick! Here is the cat!"

With one jump the city mouse reached the hole in the floor and dashed through it. After her leaped her friend.

"Well, well!" laughed the city mouse. "We got away from the cat that time."

The country mouse was so frightened that she could hardly stop shaking. At last she squeaked, "Yes! But not before the cat snapped off part of my tail!"

The city mouse wiggled her long tail. "When you live in the city," she told her friend, "you can't be slow. If you are slow, the fierce cat will gobble you up."

The country mouse was still frightened. "Good-by," she cried. "I'm going back to the country and my house of straw. I'll have only seeds and plants to eat. But fine food is not everything. It is much better to live a long time in the country than a short time in the city."

So back to the country she went. She was glad to live in her little straw house and eat seeds and plants ever after.

A Clever Fox

One morning a fox started off with an empty bag on his back. When he saw a bee, the fox thought of a clever way to fill the bag.

He caught the bee easily. He put it in the bag and went on until he came to a house. There he knocked on the door. An old woman opened it.

"I'm on my way to town," said the fox. "May I leave this bag here for a while?"

"You surely may," the woman replied.

The fox handed the bag to the woman. "I'm going to market now," he told her. "Don't open the bag while I'm gone."

Then he started down the path.

After the fox had gone, the old woman took the bag into the house. As she set it down, she heard a buzz. "There is something in that bag," she said. "I wonder if it's something useful. I shall see for myself what it is."

The woman opened the bag just a little bit. But that little bit was wide enough for the bee to crawl out. It buzzed off through the window. A hen snapped at it and gobbled it up.

After a while the fox returned for the bag. Quickly he looked inside. Then he said in a fierce voice, "Where is the bee that was in here? What have you done with it?"

The poor old woman began to cry. "I opened the bag just a little bit," she told the fox in a squeaky voice. "The bee got out, and my hen ate it."

The fox pretended to be angry. "Then you must give me your hen," he snapped.

"It shall be yours," cried the woman, hurrying to obey him.

She put her hen in the empty bag and gave it to the fox. He hung the bag on his back and trotted away.

Soon the sly fox knocked on the door of another house. He spoke to the lass who opened the door. "I'm on my way to the market," he said. "May I leave this bag here for a while?"

"You surely may," replied the lass.

The fox gave the bag to the lass. He said, "Don't open this while I'm gone."

Then off he went toward the market.

The lass took the bag into the house. When she set it on the floor, she saw it wiggle. "I wonder what wiggly thing is in this bag," she said. "I shall see."

She opened the bag just the least bit, but the hen got out. It squawked once and ran into the yard. A pet sheep gave a loud ba-a-a and scared the hen away.

Soon the fox returned for the bag. He opened it and looked inside. "Where is my hen?" he snapped at the poor lass.

"Oh-o!" she cried. "There was some queer, wiggly thing in the bag. I wanted to see what the queer thing was. I had hardly opened the bag when a hen flew out. My pet sheep scared it off."

The fox looked very angry. "Then you must give me your sheep," he snapped.

"It shall be yours," said the lass.

She hurried to obey. She put her pet sheep in the empty bag and gave it to the fox. Then he trotted down the path.

By and by the fox knocked on the door of another house. A tall lad opened it.

"I am going to market," said the fox. "May I leave this bag here for a while?"

"You surely may," the lad answered.

The fox handed the bag to the lad and said, "Don't open this while I'm gone."

And off trotted the fox.

As the lad set the bag down, he saw it shake. Then he heard a strange sound.

"A queer, wiggly, ba-a-a-ing thing is in this bag," said the lad. "I shall see for myself what it is."

He opened the bag to look inside, and out jumped the sheep. Off it ran. The lad's younger brother dashed after it, but it got away.

At sundown the fox came back for the bag. He looked inside it. But as before the bag was empty.

Again the fox looked angry. "Where is the sheep that was in here?" he snapped.

"Oh-o!" cried the lad. "I had hardly opened the bag when the sheep jumped out. My little brother chased it, but it got away."

"Then you must give me your brother," said the fox.

"He shall be yours," said the lad, "but let me say good-by to him first."

Now the lad was as clever as the fox. With a sly grin on his face, he took the bag and went into another room. There his brother was playing with a toy clown. A fierce dog lay beside the little boy.

The lad put the dog in the empty bag and carried it to the fox.

The fox lifted the heavy bag and hung it on his back. Then off he went.

On his way home the fox began singing and boasting to himself.

"I'm really very clever," he said. "I started out with just an empty bag. Now I have a bag with a small boy inside it. A boy will be useful to me. He'll cook my supper tonight and every night. I'll live like a king!"

The fox could hardly wait to get home. When he did, he set the heavy bag down and opened it wide.

Out leaped the fierce dog!

The fox gave a frightened cry. Then off he raced, with the dog close behind.

This fox was not so clever after all. For no one has seen him since that day.

The New Kettle

One day a wife said to her husband, "Tom, this kettle is no longer useful. Go to the market and buy a new one. I want to cook turnips for supper tonight."

So the husband went to the market and got a large black kettle. He hung it on his arm and started home.

The kettle was heavy, and the husband huffed and puffed as he carried it. He set it on the ground and lay down to rest.

While the man lay resting, he suddenly saw the kettle's three short legs. "Why didn't I see your legs before?" he asked the kettle. "You have three legs. I've only two. Yet I have been carrying you. That is hardly fair. It would be fairer if you had carried me. At least you ought to carry me the rest of the way."

The man sat down in the iron kettle. "Now start walking," he told it. "Make yourself useful."

But the heavy iron kettle stood still in the middle of the road. It wouldn't take even one step.

The man spoke again to the big kettle. "Didn't you hear me?" he said. "I told you to make yourself useful. Start to walk now or we won't get home tonight."

Try as he would, the man could not get the iron kettle to move.

The man grew very angry because the kettle would not obey him. He jumped up and stamped his foot.

"I see you do not mean to carry me!" he shouted. "You want me to carry you all the way. But I shall not do it!

"You have three good legs. I've only two. So why should I keep on carrying you? You must use your own legs to get to my house."

The man told the kettle where he lived. Then he left the kettle and started home by himself.

When the man reached his house, his wife asked to see the new kettle.

"Oh, it will be here sometime tonight," said the husband.

"How will the kettle get here tonight by itself?" asked the wife.

"It will walk on its own three legs," said the husband. "I have only two legs. Yet I carried that heavy iron kettle the best part of the way home.

"Now it's the kettle's turn to help me. The least it can do is to walk on its own legs the rest of the way. So I told it to walk home by itself."

The woman stamped her foot. "You clown!" she squealed. "Why did you send the kettle home by itself? I need it right now to cook the turnips."

"Please don't quarrel about the kettle," begged the husband. "It will have to use its own iron legs. It will have to learn to obey me."

"Tell me where you left that kettle!" shouted the housewife.

The man did not want to tell. But at last he said, "Near the high bridge."

His wife hurried off. Before long she was back with the heavy iron kettle.

"Why are you carrying that big kettle instead of making it walk?" the husband asked. "I told it to walk by itself."

"Yes, I know," said the wife, huffing and puffing. "I was afraid it might obey you. If it had started walking by itself, the kettle might have gone back to the market instead of walking here to us."

Gray Owl and the Rabbits

One winter day the winds blew cold, and the first snow fell in the forest. By afternoon a deep snow lay all over the ground. Then the forest animals could find hardly any food. Most of them had to eat dry seeds and plants that they had stored away.

But Gray Owl did not eat such things. When it grew dark, he flew off to hunt for a rabbit or at least a fat mouse.

Through the forest flew the owl. His wings carried him back and forth over trees and bushes. At first he saw only the cold snow that lay everywhere. Then his bright eyes saw a squirrel eating a nut. Down he swooped to snap it up, but he was too late. The squirrel got away.

As the night went on, the winds blew even colder. The owl found nothing for his dinner, and at last he turned to fly back to his home in an oak tree.

On the way, the gray-feathered hunter saw two rabbits crawling under a bush. Down he swooped!

Gray Owl caught one frightened rabbit in his right foot, and one in his left foot. Then he tried to fly off with them. But his wings were not strong enough to lift himself and the two heavy rabbits.

When the poor rabbits tried to wiggle away, the fierce gray bird held them fast. They couldn't leap away from him, but at least they could crawl.

So instead of being carried off by the hunter, the two rabbits were drawing him along on the ground.

Suddenly a great horned owl swooped low and said, "Listen, Gray Owl! Let go of one rabbit. Take only one."

Gray Owl would not listen to the wise words of the great horned owl. Instead he held on to both rabbits as they pulled him through the snow.

"Take only one! Take only one!" the great horned owl cried again.

Gray Owl was too proud of his catch to obey. "I caught them both," he said. "I'll eat them both."

All at once the frightened rabbits saw a big rock ahead. One rabbit ran to the right of the rock. The other rabbit ran to the left of it.

Bump! Gray Owl banged straight into the rock. He let go of the rabbits, and away they leaped.

So instead of getting a good dinner for himself, Gray Owl, the mighty hunter, got only a big bump on his head.

A One-Legged Goose

Once there was a jolly prince who loved to eat. One day he told his cook to roast a goose for dinner.

The cook dashed off to obey. He soon found a fine, fat goose. He picked off its feathers and washed it clean. Then he put the heavy goose in a pan and popped it into the brick oven to roast.

By dinnertime the goose was done. So with one swoop the proud cook took it from the oven and set it on the kitchen table.

"M-m-m!" said the cook. "How fine that goose looks! How good it smells! But I wonder if it is good enough for a king's son. I ought to take at least one bite to see how good it is."

He leaned over and swiftly pulled a leg off the roast goose. Then he gobbled up the leg.

After the cook had eaten the leg, the poor man felt afraid. He wondered what the prince would do when he learned why his roast goose had only one leg.

The frightened cook could think of only one thing to do. He turned the goose to keep the prince from seeing that a part of it was gone. Then he marched out of the kitchen and set the roasted bird on the prince's table.

Soon the prince came to eat his dinner. Even before he sat down, he saw that a leg of the goose was missing.

"Cook!" he roared. "Why didn't you roast all the goose? What happened to the other leg?"

The unhappy cook did not know what to say. For a few seconds he thought very hard. Then he smiled. "Oh," he said. "This goose had only one leg."

The angry prince cried, "A one-legged goose! There is no such thing!"

The clever cook suddenly remembered something he had seen the night before. "Come to the river with me tonight," he begged the prince. "There you will see many one-legged geese."

"Very well," snapped the prince. "I'll go with you. But if you can't show me at least one other one-legged goose, you are going to be in great trouble."

The prince sat down at the table and swiftly ate every bit of his dinner. Then he and his cook set off for the river.

On the bank were seven geese. Each goose had its head under one wing and one leg pulled up into its feathers.

Now the cook had seen the geese at the river the night before. He had seen them hide their heads and draw up one leg when they went to sleep.

"Look, dear Prince," he said. "It is just as I told you. Those seven geese have only one leg each."

The prince walked close to the geese. He leaned over and shouted, "B-oo-oo!"

The prince's fierce shout frightened the sleepy geese. Down came their legs, and up came their heads. Then they moved swiftly into the water.

"There!" cried the prince to his cook. "What do you think of that? Do you still say those geese have one leg each?"

"Well, dear Prince," replied the cook, "if you had shouted at the roast goose, it, also, might have had two legs."

The prince smiled at his clever cook. Then both men began to laugh. And they kept on laughing for a year and a day.

Forest Friends

Long ago a crow and a mouse lived in the same tree in a forest. In a nearby lake lived their good friend, a turtle.

One day a deer came to the tree and cried, "Crow! Please let me live under this tree. I am afraid a hunter will kill me. With a bird who squawks like you, I shall never be afraid."

The crow swiftly called the turtle and the mouse. The three animals decided to let the deer live under the tree and be their good friend.

For many days the four friends lived together in the forest. But one day all the grass around the tree was gone, and the deer went off to look for food.

That evening the deer did not return.

Early the next morning the crow said, "Perhaps something happened to Deer."

"Fly low over the land," the mouse said in his squeaky voice. "Try to find Deer."

The crow flew swiftly away, looking at the land below. At last, swooping very low, he saw the deer. It lay trapped in strong ropes.

"How did you get caught, my friend?" asked the crow. "You are too quick of foot to be caught like this."

The deer looked sad as he answered, "I saw some ears of corn in the grass. But instead of wondering why the corn was there, I tried to get it and fell into this trap. Give my love to Mouse and to Turtle. Tell them I shall never forget the wonderful times we've had."

The crow flew off to tell the mouse and the turtle what had happened to the deer.

"Oh!" cried the mouse. "We must not let the hunter kill our good friend. I'll run to the trap and bite the ropes in two. I'll free Deer before sunset tonight."

The mouse ran to the trap and began biting through the ropes. When the deer was finally free, the two happy animals started to leave the trap.

Just then they saw the turtle crawling toward the pile of ropes.

The surprised mouse asked the turtle why he had come.

"I wanted to help," said the turtle.

"Thank you, my friend," said the deer. "But Mouse set me free.

"Now let us all go home. Turtle, you must follow Mouse and me as swiftly as you can, or the hunter will kill you."

Just then the animals heard someone coming. It was the hunter drawing near. The mouse and the deer dashed off. But the turtle was too slow to get very far.

The hunter saw the cut ropes of the trap and felt sure that he had lost a deer. Then he saw the poor turtle. At least he could have a turtle for his supper. He took a small rope from his pocket, tied the turtle's feet, and carried it away.

When the turtle did not come home, the other three friends were very unhappy.

"He wanted to help me," said the deer. "Now he will be killed instead of me."

Suddenly the mouse thought of a clever way to help the turtle. He told his two friends what they should do, and each of them went off to obey him.

The deer ran through the bushes ahead of the hunter without being seen. Then the deer dropped to the ground, acting as if it had been killed.

The crow swooped down and sat on the deer's horns.

The mouse ran through the grass behind the hunter.

The hunter saw the deer ahead of him and thought it had been killed. He put down the turtle to get the deer. At once the mouse ran up to the turtle and bit through the rope tied around its feet.

As soon as the hunter reached the deer, the crow lifted its wings and flew at the hunter's face.

The hunter jumped back, and the deer leaped swiftly away.

"Something very queer is happening here," said the hunter to himself. "I'm sure that deer wasn't a live one. Yet it leaped away right before my eyes."

The hunter ran back to get the turtle, but it had gone also.

"Something queer surely is happening," thought the man. "A turtle cannot walk with its feet tied, but that one got away by itself."

Out of the forest ran the frightened hunter as fast as he could go.

Before long the crow, the mouse, the turtle, and the deer were home again.

The deer said, "Oh, how useful it is to have good friends! That hunter would surely have killed me if I had not had such good friends."

"You are right, Deer," said the turtle. "I'm sure I would have been killed and eaten if my friends had not saved me."

The crow nodded his head. "Friends must always stick together and help one another," he said. "If they do, then all will be well."

The content of *More Friends Old and New,* Book Two, Part Two, of The New Cathedral Basic Reading Program, is organized into three units. These units represent areas of interest that are attractive to most young children, both in real life and in books. In Unit I, "Neighborhood Friends," the stories move from place to place in a setting clearly recognizable as the urban community of St. Mark's parish. The stories of Unit II, "Animal Friends," reflect the interest that youngsters have in domesticated and wild animals, and provide more varied settings than are found in the first unit. In Unit III, "Storybook Friends," the stories are either folk tales—a type of tale that appeared earlier in Book One, *More Fun with Our Friends*—or fables.

Various features of *More Friends Old and New* raise it to a new level of maturity in this series. The most obvious is the format of the book. The content is arranged in standard paragraphs, and it is printed in lines of equal length, as books for adults are. Pages without illustration occur more frequently than at previous levels, and in several cases two of these pages are consecutive.

Further marks of maturity will be found in the style in which the stories are written. Sentence patterns are more involved than in the preceding books, and the proportion of complex and compound-complex sentences increases considerably. Narrative and descriptive passages are longer and more numerous. Time and causal relationships are more fully and clearly expressed with the introduction of *while* and *since.* Illustrations bear less and less of the burden of telling the story until, in Unit III, all the stories are virtually independent of the illustrative material.

Most important in the advancing maturity of *More Friends Old and New* is the variety of interpretative skills demanded by the content. The ability to anticipate events is developed through many stories, most of which require more careful noting of details, more intricate interrelating of those details, and more complex thinking about them than the stories at earlier levels did. Problem-solving processes of different kinds are a significant part of the web of interpretative skills developed in *More Friends Old and New.* "The Wooden Fence" (page 43), for example, calls for a mechanical solution; "The Quarrel" (page 178), a logical solution; and "Forest Friends" (page 257), a combined logical and psychological solution. Many of the tales of Unit III provide ideal material for practice in developing a generalization based on facts or behavior presented.

The procedures in the *Guidebook* for *More Friends Old and New* help children make rapid growth toward independence in reading. Through the skills, abilities, and understandings strengthened at this level, children will more fully enjoy the stories in the basic reader, as well as the books and stories they choose for their personal reading. In the *Think-and-Do Book* these same skills, abilities, and understandings are reinforced as pupils apply them to different kinds of content.

More Friends Old and New introduces 358 new words. Each one is used a minimum of six times, without a gap of more than five pages between the first two of its uses. This book also continues to use the 563 words introduced at previous levels. Any words that were new in Book Two, Part One, *Friends Old and New*, are further repeated in Book Two, Part Two. Words used ten or more times in Book Two, Part One, appear at least once in Book Two, Part Two.

Besides the 358 new words mentioned above, there are 120 new forms of known words in *More Friends Old and New*. These forms, which are not counted as new, include the following: words in which spelling changes occur before an ending or a suffix (the final consonant doubled, the final *y* changed to *i*, or final *e* dropped); words made by adding or dropping the endings *es* and *er* or *est* of comparison, the suffixes *er* (of agent) and *y* with or without a spelling change in the root word; and contractions with two letters omitted.

In the list below, the 358 new words in this book are printed in black, the 120 new forms in blue. Children can identify the 339 starred words by combining context clues with word analysis. The number and kind of starred words indicate pupils' rapid growth in independence.

Vocabulary List

Neighborhood Friends

5. ....
6. ....
7. bike*
   Tramp*
8. ice*
   eyes
   sliding*
   you've*

9. muddy*
wet*
10. while*
sadly
we'll*
having*
11. smiled*
David
later*
lunches*
12. Katy
enough
13. opened
happened

---

14. valentines
Ellen
living*
15. ate*
face*
16. oven
decided
17. through
kitchen
18. burned*
really

---

19. block*
baseball*
player*
we've*
20. Jerry*
hope*
I'd*
21. sure
bat*
22. hit*
second
batters*
23. raced*
rest*
tripped*
24. mean*
George

---

25. week*
breakfast
sunny*
26. might*
glass*
you'd*
27. across
toward
something's*
28. hi*
kicking*
stepped*
29. pretend
pat*
30. porch*
reached*
we'd*

---

31. Tony*
summer
they'd*
32. carry
whispered
33. corner
table
34. gift*
hanging*
parties*
higher*
35. replied
pink*
36. floor*
pointed
37. brought*
seven

---

38. mystery
together
sitting*
39. questions
notes*
40. young
wrote*
harder*
41. remember
gate*
42. unhappy
feet*
he's*
misses*

---

43. wooden
Steve*
44. standing*
45. waved*
46. hole*
yet*
47. low*
48. friendly
part*

---

49. missionary
country
50. build
nailed*
worker*
51. river
knew*
52. even
hold*
tries*
53. quiet
teach*
teachers*
54. real*
pray*

---

55. afternoon
bank*
taking*
56. dime*
save*
he'll*
57. bus*
myself
58. shake*
egg*
pennies*
saving*

---

59. write*
eight
60. drive*
carts*
markers*
61. oil
meet*
62. filled*
handy
using*
they'll*
easier*
dropped*
63. throwing*
grinned*
patted*
64. few
mouths
carried*
grinning*

---

65. owns
held*
66. city
ago
oldest*
younger*
67. engine
feel*
owner*
68. brick*
almost
hoping*

69. . . . .
driving*

70. pool*
swim*

71. clock*

72. arms*
lucky*
swimming*

73. pocket
trunks*
good-luck*

74. . . . .

75. deep*

76. short*

77. . . . .

78. . . . .
letting*

79. flag*
parade
grin*

80. certainly
tomorrow

81. bad*
interesting
hardest*

82. surely*
trouble

83. since
finally

84. forgot

85. yelled*
words*

86. supposed
crowd

87. led*
rocking*
troubling*

88. huge*
begged*

89. earth
sky*
cities*

90. slowly*
writing*

91. taken

92. . . . .

Animal Friends

93. . . . .

94. gloves
grass*

95. chin*
track*

96. excitedly
belonged

97. followed
oak*
pup*

98. branch*
excited*
chinned*

99. shut*
carefully

100. fall*
lake*

101. peanut
butter
boxes*

102. kept*
straws*
putting*
glasses*

103. closed*
caught

104. voice
katydid

105. covered
piled*

106. wrong*

107. stood*
puppies*

108. quickly*
blew*
icy*
shaking*

109. roast*
she'll*

110. fair*
believe
ponies*

111. coax*
offer
closer*

112. rushed*
lifted*

113. . . . .
driver*

114. easily*
trotted*

115. rode*
free*

116. camping*
bait*

117. pail*
grabbed*

118. strange
woods*

119. seemed*
sandy*

120. raccoon
eaten
there'll*
grab*

121. wolf
elephant

122. third*
exciting*
123. deer*
drink*
124. ....
125. ....

---

126. forth*
newest*
127. ....
keeper*
leaving*
waving*
128. bars*
129. such*

---

130. blueberries
nodded*
older*
131. cupcakes
pan*
baking*
blueberry*
132. hot*
cool*
133. sudden*
134. ....

---

135. curly*
paw*
Jimmy*
136. ....
curls*
137. ....
138. I'd
Rags*
139. ....
140. ....

---

141. ....
142. most
scary*
petted*
143. feathers
ahead
144. leaped*
nodding*
145. loud*
shirt*
146. ....

---

147. bright*
148. ladder
roared*
149. hose*
above
hopped*
louder*
150. against*
longer*
151. setting*
wall*
set*
152. felt*

---

153. cage*
learn*
Sonny*
whistling*
hopping*
154. number
155. spoke*
songs*
156. flew*
garage
157. chance
alone
158. happily*

---

159. joke*
Dick*
160. sound*
grunting*
161. chased*
162. beside
163. ought*
chasing*
164. ....

---

165. fox*
stronger*
youngest*
166. act*
grow*
167. ....
Foxy*
168. wild
strong*
169. bushes*
foxes*
170. ....

Storybook Friends

171. ....
172. hare*
hedgehog
bush*
173. turnips
angry
sooner*
174. wife*
row*
175. bottom
popped*
176. dashed*
huffed*
pop*
177. full*
boast*

---

178. quarrel
proud*

179. owl*
fruit
180. crossing
tall*
lowest*
181. ....
finest*
182. forest

---

183. skipped*
evening
grassy*
184. also
cries*
185. great
186. foolish
187. sting*
skip*

---

188. pot*
chimney
Johnny*
189. ....
190. middle
sing*
191. sly*
192. ....

---

193. Alonzo
Clop-Clop*
194. ....
195. ....
196. ....
197. ....
198. Yip-Yip*
199. ....
200. ....
201. ....

---

202. landed*
queer*
203. life*
204. below
205. king*
lion
barred*
206. ....
207. shall

---

208. hung*
supper
209. bite*
bushy*
nod*
210. wide*
grew*
biting*
colder*
211. ....
shorter*

---

212. crawl*
squeaky*
213. warmer
geese*
cooler*
warm*
squeaked*
214. returned
wings*
215. straight*
joking*

---

216. terrible
churn*
217. cream*
knocked*

218. stamping*
draw*
219. leaned*
rope*
220. roof*
bridge*
221. cook*
horns*
222. gruff*
223. ....

---

224. ugly
troll*
shortest*
hiding*
225. trap*
gobble
226. frightened
227. bit*
loudest*
228. hardly

---

229. seeds*
plants*
230. wiggle
clever*
231. fierce
snapped*
232. ....

---

233. empty
bag*
234. market
useful
235. obey
lass*
236. least*
wiggly*
237. lad*
238. ....

239. lay*
heavy
240. tonight

---

241. kettle
husband
242. iron
fairer*
243. ....
244. itself
245. instead

---

246. hunt*
247. swooped*
snap*
hunter*
248. ....
249. ....
250. ....
mighty*

---

251. prince*
one-legged*
252. swiftly*
253. ....
254. ....
255. ....
256. ....

---

257. kill*
258. ....
trapped*
259. ....
260. ....
261. ....
262. ....
263. ....

Acknowledgments

Grateful acknowledgment is hereby given for the right to adapt and use the following copyrighted material:

"The Wooden Fence" adapted from *Stevie Finds a Way* by Ruth Liebers and Lillian Rothenberg. Copyright © 1955, 1958 by Abingdon Press, Nashville, Tenn. Used by permission of the authors and publishers.

"A Good Name for a Dog" from "The Telltale Tracks" by Margaret Hockersmith in *Jack and Jill*, October 1960. © 1960 by The Curtis Publishing Company, Philadelphia. Used by special permission of the author and publishers.

"The Day Before the Fair" from "Runaway Ponies" by Mildred Bair Lissfelt in *The Instructor*, September 1955. Used by permission of the author.

"Jim Goes Camping" from "The Mystery of the Missing Minnows" by Margaret O. Slicer in *Jack and Jill*, July 1959. © 1959 by the Curtis Publishing Company, Philadelphia. Used by special permission of the author and publishers.

"A Wrong Guess" from "The Cookies" by Ruth Bishop Juline. From *Children's Activities*. By permission of Highlights for Children, Inc., Columbus, Ohio, owner of the copyright.

"The Visiting Dog" from "Little Dog Lost" by Marguerite Aspinwall in *Stories*, August 8, 1954. Copyright 1954 by W. L. Jenkins. Used by permission of the author and The Westminster Press, Philadelphia.

"Firehouse Cat" from "The Firehouse Cat" by Bianca Bradbury. By permission of Highlights for Children, Inc., Columbus, Ohio, owner of the copyright. From *Children's Activities*.

"Sonny" from "Sam the Parakeet" by Mildred Bair Lissfelt in *The Instructor*, April 1959. Used by permission of the author.

"A Joke on Sandy" from "The Cookies" by Ruth Bishop Juline. From *Children's Activities*. By permission of Highlights for Children, Inc., Columbus, Ohio, owner of the copyright.

"The Baby Fox" from "Rusty's Return to the Hills" by Ann King in *Jack and Jill*, September 1947. © 1947 by The Curtis Publishing Company, Philadelphia. Used by special permission of the publishers and of Mrs. Hosking Jensen.

"The One-Legged Goose" from "The Gypsy and the Goose" in *Rumanian Folk Tales* (original title, *Pacala and Tandala*), translated by Jean Ure. By special permission of Franklin Watts, Inc., New York, and Methuen & Co., Ltd., London.

"Forest Friends" from "Deep in the Forest" by Ramji in *Stories*, November 25, 1956. Copyright 1956 by W. L. Jenkins. Used by permission of The Westminster Press, Philadelphia.

3 4 5 6 7 8 9 10 11 12 13 14 15 16 17 18 19 20 C 75 74 73 72 71 70 69 68 67 66 65